To ~~Maryann~~

Hope you enjoy
my first novel!

♡

2022
J

D1536898

Under the Oak Tree

To
graeme (cracker)

3–
2021

Under the Oak Tree

By

Gretchen Dubit

© 2021 by Gretchen L. Weiss Dubit

All rights reserved. This book or any portion thereof may not be reproduced or used in any manner whatsoever without the express written permission of the publisher except for the use of brief quotations in a book review.

ISBN 1499210442 (paperback)

My Mom and Dad, under the Oak Tree, Circa 1992

For my father, who lived this story.
For my mother, who left us too soon.
And for my aunt, Marie, who was a legend to us all.

The author visiting Opelousas, April 1971

Dr. C. A. Weiss
Reymond Building
Baton Rouge, La.

Little boy tho you're back
Still we must scold
For you are only a baby
Just four years old.

New York is so far
With its cold and snow
While way down here
The roses grow.

Da-Da raised dahlias
So pretty and big
He needs you here
To help him dig.

In Aunt Nellie's yard
Where May flowers grow
They bloomed for you there
By the fence row.

They had so many flowers
They took them away
Out to Roselawn
On All Saint's Day.

Grandmother is lonesome
For you are not here
To tease and to love her
And bring her good cheer.

Your flight thru France
Must have been a sight
Riding dirty trains
With out any lights.

Up stairs and down tracks
With boxes and bags
Holding on Mom-ees coat tail
So your steps wouldn't lag.

What a big man, son
You turned out to be
The pride and the joy
Of adventurous Mom-ee.

Any way you take it
You had a fine trip
Except coming back
On that rocking ole ship.

All over the deck
On that rolling sea
You carried the pan
For your poor sick Mom-ee.

Dr. C. A. Weiss
Reymond Building
Baton Rouge, La.

Now you speak French
But we no "Sa-Va"
So what can we do
When you come home to stay.

So get yourself back
Leave that French parlez-vous
And fish with your da-da
Down on the Bayou.

11/7/39

ONE

Infamy Is Not the
Same as Fame

My brother, sister, and I pictured with our Great Aunt Marie, Circa 1978

I ALWAYS THOUGHT that people involved in history-making events were automatically rich and famous. I thought they told the story of that far-off relative who struck gold or invented the safety pin and sat around for the rest of their lives telling the story of that family member who did something noteworthy, living off the royalties. I thought a famous relative meant you rested on your laurels and simply amassed a fortune by retelling the story to anyone who would listen. It was not that way for my great-aunt Marie and the rest of us, for whom life was forever changed when her beloved sister's husband was accused of committing an act that would change the course of many lives. There are so many events that can change the course of things, like a change in jobs or a move to a new town. A man I never knew, named Carl Austin Weiss, changed the trajectory for me and many others in our large southern family.

I know who will be interested in hearing the story of the sixty-one bullets in the capitol building on that late September eve by their age, education, and profession. Anyone interested in history is surely riveted, but aside from social studies teachers, history professors, or those with knowledge of American history of the 1930s, those who live in the South might find the story of interest. Specifically those from the iconic boot-shaped state of Louisiana might want to hear the story. I can tell a Louisiana accent from that of Texas, Alabama, Mississippi, and other states south of the Mason-Dixon Line. In those southern states, the drawl is long and drawn out, but the Louisiana accent—although I have never lived there but spent a week there each year until I was eighteen—is one that I can discern readily for its slow, resounding "Yaaawwl." On my last visit to my father's home state for a family wedding, my cousin Al proudly told me that Louisiana is a different part of the world, so different that he proclaimed it should be necessary to carry a passport to cross state lines into Cajun country. Cajuns are not made; they are born.

I often ponder how different life would have been had my grandfather, Carl, not been in that place at that time, had he not been in the capitol building in Baton Rouge that night. I wonder what might have happened had he, the twenty-nine-year-old father of a newborn, not gone into that lit-up building on a hot summer evening to hear the legislature vote on an amendment that would gerrymander his father-in-law, Henry Pavy, out of his judgeship. Would I be living the life of a southern belle in southern Louisiana, the daughter of a prominent family of physicians and lawyers? That young doctor really had no business in the capitol that night; he should have been home, perhaps reading a story to his newborn son. The age-old question is why Carl Austin Weiss stepped out of his car and into the capitol building in Baton Rouge on that fateful night. He was not a killer.

Two

Hero or Hit Man?

Carl Austin Weiss, age 29 1935

WHEN I TELL the story of my infamous grandfather to people, especially if they know the story and have a grasp of history, they look at me quizzically. Either they do not know the story at all, or they have enough of a grasp of history to wonder just how this tragic and far-off story fits into where we are standing now. People involved in infamy do not live next door. Or do they? It is like talking to the daughter of Bonnie and Clyde or meeting the son of Son of Sam. But my grandfather was not a gun-slinging bank robber or a man who heard voices. Carl Austin Weiss was a young physician in the prime of his life, surrounded by family and friends, yet his place in a historic, tragic event would change the course of many lives, including mine. His actions would drive my grandmother, Yvonne, away from the South. The name Carl Austin Weiss became synonymous with a murderer, and their lives would never be the same. New York is a place of millions, and surely she would be anonymous here, or so my grandmother thought when she chose the Big Apple for her home. My father set up a home in Garden City, a tree-lined suburb on Long Island. Only my sister was born in Louisiana, when my parents lived there shortly while my father was in the U.S. Air Force. Garden City is an incorporated village in the middle of Long Island, designed by an Irish-born millionaire who built a grand hotel that was the centerpiece of the town. It became famous for its tree-lined streets. This white-collar suburban neighborhood is where he raised his family and the place we stayed until my eventual move after college to chase a boy all the way to Colorado. Upon graduation from college, I spent two winters not using my English degree, working as a lift operator at a Vermont ski area where I met my ski patroller husband. It was a ski area romance that no one thought would last, but we were married just two years later. Only three months into our marriage and now living in Durango, Colorado, I asked my husband if he would ever consider moving back to the East Coast, to the place I knew as home. His response was an immediate, "Nope." And I knew that my life as a New Yorker was not to be. His response solidified my fear that I would have to choose between him and the life in the city that I thought I was just taking a break from. It was then I realized that I'd better make this place home despite my yearnings every summer to be near the water, the beach, and the moist air. My father had left

Louisiana; now I had left New York, and I feared that I could not go home again, just as his mother did when she left her home behind for a safer place—one that did not recognize the name Weiss. That is certainly the case now, when history fades and the principals die.

From a community college campus, far from any major metropolitan area in the desert Southwest, I tell my students where I am from and explain why I talk so fast. This community college is located in a small New Mexican city bordering the Navajo Nation and is considered an industrial hub, especially of the oil and gas industry. On my forty-five-minute drive from the more affluent town of Durango along Highway 550, the oil and gas trucks can be seen with a water cooler affixed to the bed of the truck and tall flags that are an informal safety device employed by the oil field workers to avoid collisions when they race around in the unpaved, hilly badlands where the wells are often located. During mud season these typically white Ford trucks turn brown with the sticky red dirt from rutted, well-traveled roads. My community college is at the crossroads of a bustling, oil-driven city, and the rural Navajo reservation, where there are no road signs, and the road system are so primitive that GPS does not work here. I drive across the border from Colorado to New Mexico to teach composition to an underserved population on a beautiful southwest-styled campus with white stucco buildings surrounded by xeriscaping to respect the lack of water in this part of the United States.

The Southwest is characteristically laid back; it is a place where people come to soak up the mountain air and get away from the hustle and bustle of life in the city. If you want something done fast, it isn't going to happen here. Asking someone to rush it is a sure sign of an outsider. People come to southern Colorado to escape things and people. Long pauses and even-longer stories are common here, and my fast pace and quick-witted tongue are the first things people notice. I tell my students that I grew up just a thirty-minute train ride from the World Trade Center, and my hometown has the unfortunate distinction of having more people killed in the World Trade Center attacks than any other town on Long Island. They wonder how I left that place for this, how I left a place they long to go visit and wound up in a place many wish to get away from. New Mexico is called the Land of Enchantment, but my students, who are largely from the Navajo reservation, jokingly say that they come to Farmington for vacation but stay because of incarceration. The rate of incarcerated Native Americans is considerably higher than that of any other race in New Mexico. While Santa Fe is one of the wealthiest counties in America, New Mexico still rates as one of the poorest states in the nation. The daily drive to work from my home in the mountains of Colorado takes me past rural water projects, coal-fired power plants, and finally to the edge of the Navajo reservation where many come from a world that has recently found running water and electricity. Then the students wonder how I left anywhere for this place.

How we find our way anywhere is a game of luck—the drop of a pin on a map. Or is it? This is the story of an untimely death that changed the course of events in such a way that living in the South became impossible. And this is the story of how the Long and Weiss families became inextricably linked forever.

Born and raised in the suburbs of Long Island, I was never

far from the shriek of the high-speed railroad that whizzed men and women wearing dark suits, with a *New York Times* or a *Wall Street Journal* tucked into their armpits, to jobs on Wall Street and other parts of the city that never sleeps. But my landing here might not have happened this way if Carl Austin Weiss, a twenty-nine-year-old practicing physician, had not been lured by the brightly lit courthouse, curious as to the goings-on of that summer evening. Or if the house call he had made earlier in the evening to tend to a sick patient had lasted a bit longer. Whatever lured him into the Louisiana courthouse that evening changed the trajectory for many. The old expression "curiosity killed the cat" rings true here for man, not feline.

My grandfather, Carl Weiss, was a spectacled man who lived in a small clapboard house with his bride, Yvonne, and their infant son, my father, Carl Weiss Jr. It was directly across from the Louisiana State Capitol, just a two-hour drive along the I-10 corridor from Yvonne's birthplace, Opelousas. The third-oldest town in Louisiana, Opelousas's slogan is "Perfectly Seasoned," due to it once being the home of the late culinary great Chef Paul Prudhomme and creole-seasoning entrepreneur Tony Chachere. But in the early days, it was a racially divided town in an agricultural part of the States with a history of prostitution, just a stopping point on the way to New Orleans. I remember the rows and rows of soybeans tucked neatly beneath the red dirt and the rows and rows of dilapidated tenement homes. It was a world away from the life I knew on Long Island.

My grandfather was born into a medical family; his father had been a doctor and his grandfather before him. So he fell into the family business too, and his education as a medical doctor brought him from Tulane Medical School in New Orleans to a short stint practicing in Vienna to Paris, where he lived from 1925 to 1929. There he befriended the writer Ernest Hemingway, author of *A Farewell to Arms*, which refers to a young doctor who treated him in Paris. After his travels in Europe, Carl came home and back into the bosom of his family as a fourth-generation doctor, a well-educated man of healing, to practice in Louisiana. He carried a leather doctor's bag that had belonged to his father before him. This was a family of tradition; nothing was left to chance. They followed a strict code of family conduct, and he did not stray off the path but continued his trajectory of being the third doctor in a line named Carl. This is what makes this story all the more mystifying.

The Louisiana Capitol, the tallest capitol building in the country, which Huey Long built as a shrine to himself, is a stone's throw from his namesake bridge and across town from the university that bears his name on buildings and academic halls. It is no wonder my grandmother left. The signs are everywhere. And so when I tell my students the story of the man whose untimely death left my father fatherless, I too wonder how things beyond our control fatefully place us where we might not ordinarily go, while being in the right place is considered the result of hard work or good choices. The choices of our predecessors impact the course of each and every person's future. Every choice can have radical repercussions that reverberate for generations to come, and in the case of a young doctor in the prime of his life, he made a split-second decision to park and go in.

The lights were on in the grandest building of its time, a veritable skyscraper in Baton Rouge. That was read by my grandfather as an invitation to see what was going on in the hall at night. His wife, Yvonne, and baby, Carl, were at home, probably sleeping. They would not notice if he was gone just a bit longer; something drew him inside. We will never know what or why.

My grandfather was not interested in politics by all accounts but was affected by the Huey Long regime. Huey Long was a man of humble beginnings who became a powerful figure in Louisiana politics because of his ability to connect with the common man. He was named the Kingfish after and Amos and Andy cartoon character presumably because the character was adept at getting people to do what he wanted while it was not always in their best interest. My great-grandfather, Judge Henry Pavy, the father of Yvonne, presided over a precinct in South Louisiana and was about to lose his jurisdiction; his views were not popular with the Long political machine. By all accounts Long was a power grabber, and in those days, you were either for Long or against Long, and for those who did not play by his rules, terrible things happened. There is the story of the tomato thrown at Huey Long while at a rally in Monroe, Louisiana, an expression of disapproval of Huey's road project. That unpopular toss of a vegetable caused Long to reroute one of the thousands of miles of paved roads he added to the state and left Monroe in the dark ages. He chose a nearby town to develop instead, and money for roads and infrastructure poured in while Monroe's infrastructure fell deeper into disrepair. Huey was good to those who were good to him. Long wanted to redistribute the wealth with his "Every Man a King" slogan, but to some, he was more like a fascist who greased the palms of those who did what he asked, while those who opposed him were taken down by his loyal regime.

Judge Henry Pavy and Huey Long did not see eye to eye on things, particularly on how intent Long was on sweeping up power in his state of Louisiana. A simple vote in the courthouse that night on September 8, 1935 would gerrymander him out of office. Huey Long loved power and control, and when he saw a threat, he had the ability to change people's lives with the stroke of a pen. Redistricting meant that Henry Pavy would no longer be the esteemed judge, community member, and father of eight children who all attended the local schools. The Pavy family enjoyed the notoriety that came with a large southern family of prominence. Everyone knew or was related to the Pavy family, as Judge Henry was one of ten children from the rural town of Opelousas. They were committed members of the community. There was a Pavy Street and a school named in honor of a Pavy who taught there. They were rooted in St. Landry Parish, with Judge Pavy seated firmly at the helm. The pending vote in the courthouse that night would have rendered a popular judge unemployed and irrelevant. A man revered by his children, his family, and his community would be stripped of his judgeship. But was that motive for killing Huey Long? Was that reason enough for an otherwise-sane man to commit suicide? Surely he knew that what he was ultimately accused of doing would end in death.

And so the lights of the courthouse may have been a sign to my grandfather, announcing that something had to be done. Perhaps Huey Long would listen to reason. Instead of making a right turn into his driveway on Lakeland Drive, he stopped, parked, and walked into the Louisiana State Capitol building. The rest, as they say, is history.

THREE

A Son Is Born

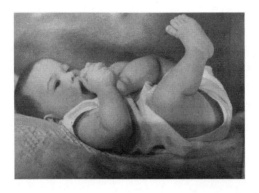

Carl Austin Weiss, Jr.. 3 months 1935

THREE MONTHS BEFORE the tragedy, Yvonne gave birth to my father, who was the first of a new generation of Pavys and enjoyed the attention of six aunts and uncles. He was given a strong family name and was the third Carl in a row, but the second Carl Austin, after his own father. There were many aunts and uncles ready and waiting to fill his childhood with camaraderie, family dinners, picnics, and the like. He was the long-awaited firstborn and already had big shoes to fill and a big name to boot. He was from a long line of doctors and would surely follow in their footsteps. Yet at just three months old, he would become fatherless, and the world would mourn the death of a man, his father, whom he never knew, yet who shaped his life in countless ways with his death. And a politician would be dead, changing the political landscape, especially in Louisiana.

To some, Huey Long was a hero for paving roads, building bridges, and creating a brand of socialism in the poor state of Louisiana with this "Every Man a King" campaign to share the wealth. To others he was a dictator, known for his ruthless ways. There were reprisals for any of his vocal opponents. Huey's ambitious road program was expected to shorten the eighty-mile trip between Baton Rouge and New Orleans from an entire day of travel to less than two hours. Ironically, the road was not complete when Long was fatally shot in Baton Rouge. The trauma surgeons summoned from New Orleans could not reach Long in time by driving along the old River Road. His bridge projects were expected to decrease the time and money needed to travel on a patched-together system of ferries, toll bridges, and makeshift water crossings. Huey Long was ambitious, but he made up his own rules, and if you challenged, questioned, or cautioned him, you had a bear on your hands. Many described him as a demagogue with an insatiable lust for power and control. Thus the connection between him and my grandfather, Judge Henry Pavy, is loose at best.

This is where the fuzziness comes into play. The judge was about to lose his job by the stroke of a pen, gerrymandering, or redistricting. Alas, that would not be all that Huey did to Judge Pavy. Long repeated to news reporters an old claim that a Pavy family member had an African American mistress and allegedly warned Judge Pavy that if Pavy continued to oppose him, Long would announce that Pavy's family was tainted with "coffee blood." In 1935 those were fighting words, and the Pavy family cherished their family name and accomplishments, in this case to the death.

Four

Leaving Opelousas Behind

THE HIGHLY PUBLICIZED death of Carl Austin Weiss at age twenty-nine was a tragedy that reverberated throughout the family for decades and left it shattered. Aunt Marie was just twenty-three and was in her first year as a history teacher. Yvonne was her oldest sister, and those fired shots in the courthouse left her a widow at age twenty-seven with a three-month-old baby—my father—to care for alone. In the confusion of the night of September 8, 1935, when shots rang out in the courthouse and Carl Austin Weiss was named the hit man, Yvonne had no choice but to accept the verdict and move on. Her dead husband was so vilified throughout Louisiana and the country that she packed up her belongings and set out for Europe, where she felt the climate for herself and her infant son would be safer. Marie was left at home, where she had to defend her brother-in-law to the masses and hold her name and head high, for in the South, a name means everything.

My husband is fascinated by the South for many reasons. He tells the story of my family's plunge to infamy to anyone who will listen, and he loves an audience, while I save it for those for whom it has some relevance, who have a sense of history and the importance that the event holds. Many have said that Huey Long would have run for president against FDR, had he not been killed. I have learned that there are certain people who will be fascinated by the telling of it, and those who will not understand the relevance of it will have no idea why I am telling the story of a murder and a dead man. On those I will have wasted my breath. Those who love true-crime stories might be interested.

There are fewer and fewer people today who will remember the story, as happens when time marches on and those who lived during those times in history have faded away. The stories disappear to make way for new ones. Now I rely solely on those from Louisiana and those who know history to be a willing audience. Robert, a history professor at the college where I work, just happened to be sitting in the adjunct office where I was preparing a lesson for my students during my absence. My absence was a long weekend to Louisiana for the seventy-fifth anniversary of the Huey Long shooting. Being a history teacher and well versed in the event, Robert was equally amazed by the story and by my lot in life at this particular moment. It was that quizzical look that forced me to elaborate on the chain of events that brought me here to this spot today. As we talked, this historian prodded me to get writing; he felt I had a story to tell, simply because of the chain of events, the death of a man I never knew, the father my father never met, and the places we arrive as a result of the actions of others. What if Huey Long had been president? I would not be writing this from my office as a writing instructor in northern New Mexico. The events of our lives, whether they be noteworthy or not, have a profound effect on the offspring of others for generations to come.

When I was planning to leave home and choose a college, I fancied myself going back to Louisiana, a place filled with fond memories and family. My mother told me I would never make it as a southern belle. She said they ate northerners alive. This was just one more example of her disdain for the South. She had to work hard to earn respect from the southern family she'd married into and found southern charm akin to passive-aggressive behavior. She was accustomed to saying it like it was, like it or not, and was never one to sugarcoat anything. She was both loved and maligned for her no-nonsense approach. My mother was a New Yorker through and through. Even now, when my mother-in-law wants to put me in my place, she takes a swipe at New Yorkers as crass, as if she forgets my proud lineage of being from New York and knowing all the words to Frank Sinatra's song, "New York, New York."

At every wedding in New York I have ever been to, this song riles the crowd of enthusiastic New Yorkers more than any other song. My mother was a proud New Yorker and not as much a fan of the South. Perhaps it was the killing of the father-in-law and ensuing cover-up of the man she never knew and the scar it left on the family that gave her a distaste for the South.

When one's name was synonymous with a political killing, the small-town doctor's family was bound to lose.

And lose they did. There were jobs lost when the family name of Pavy was involved. A judgeship was annulled, a school principal was demoted, and a young teacher lost her job. That young teacher was my aunt, Marie. Perhaps no one was more affected by the death of that young man than Aunt Marie. She watched the heartbreak of her mama and papa, Judge Pavy and his wife, Ida Veazie, who wed in 1896. Aunt Marie, ever the sensitive one, struggled to watch the heartbreak of Yvonne, her older sister, dashed by the politics of their elders, caught in the crosshairs. The heat of the moment, when guns were fired, altered the lives of so many and for so long. The shroud that fell on the family name was hard for Aunt Marie to shoulder. So the year that she was fired as a history teacher because of her name was the year that the family fell apart, and the depths of infamy caused an irreparable wound for the once-great family.

When Aunt Marie's brother-in-law was riddled with bullets by Huey Long's overzealous bodyguards, a family was stopped in its tracks. As Senator Long lay dying, the husband of my Aunt Marie's revered older sister was implicated in the highly publicized death. The radio proclaimed a young doctor as the assailant. Many say he was named before he was positively identified. Needless to say, the world known to the Pavy family was interrupted forever. Marie Aline Pavy, my great-aunt Marie and the matriarch of a large southern family that reveled in its Acadian heritage, suffered a severe setback. A school that had been named in honor of a caring and charismatic uncle, a champion in education, was suddenly renamed so as not to reflect a name that had become synonymous with a high-profile political assassination. Her father, the Judge, as he was called even years after his death, who was at the helm of the St. Landry Parish court system for twenty years, was dethroned.

Marie Aline Pavy, sister to the alleged assassin's wife, in her second year as a teacher of Louisiana history, was suddenly forced to leave her classroom, fired for her family name. At the family homestead where she proudly announced her name, "Miss Pavy," she was now an outcast, and her favorite sister and new baby nephew were exiled. Maybe it was this dark event in history that gave the family such strength of character. Perhaps the event was the impetus for this family to become a tight-knit circle of protectors. When the shroud of villainy lifted some years later, they had not only survived such blight on the family name, but they were stronger for it, and Marie was reinstated as a teacher and taught Louisiana history to decades of students. Such was the turbulent world of Miss Marie, a southern matriarch whose roots in St. Landry Parish were as deep as those of the centuries-old oak trees encircling her home.

FIVE

The Haven on Cherry Street

(Aunt Marie on Cherry Street)

AFTER THE SHOTS were fired and the smoke had cleared, the family house on Cherry Street, situated in the middle of Opelousas, became a safe haven. Visitors drove the long drive-way, blowing the horn to announce a new arrival. Perhaps the horn-blowing tradition evolved to warn the inhabitants that a friend, not a foe, was approaching. In this house, after the shooting, many were fearful; their foundation was rocked, and the home was a place of solace. The horn-honking tradition continued for years, even into my visits to Opelousas, as a sign to Aunt Marie that the party would soon be bigger, and everyone needed a highball to celebrate. As soon as the tires rubbed against the cattle guard at the start of the driveway off of Cherry Street, it was time to start an intermittent honk reaching all the way to the whitewashed picket fence and park next to Aunt Marie's red Buick. The horn blowing was a sort of SOS call that in this case meant, "Save Our Seat" to the party. Marie would go to the screen door and open it wide like outstretched arms, ready to celebrate the arrival of any and all visitors. She loved parties.

But it would be many years till the party resumed. The dark days after her brother-in-law was posthumously accused of murder lingered for many years, and because her revered older sister and newborn son were gone across the big pond, her heart was broken. The family home in Louisiana still stead-fastly believed the murder was in error, but the inquisition was botched, and Huey Long's bodyguards were forbidden to clear up any details of what really happened that night. It would take many months to reveal that the bullets came from the gun of a bodyguard, and that Carl Austin Weiss was unarmed. Huey's last words, "That is where he hit me," would not be revealed until much later, proving that there was an assault on Huey Long by Carl Weiss that night in the capitol building after Huey Long pushed him aside and called him a "pissant" before the bodyguards unloaded their guns, with one ricochet-ing off the marble and striking Huey. Sixty-one of the bul-lets entered Carl Weiss's body. The damage done to the family name was swift and damning.

When Huey Long died on the operating table, and Yvonne was forced to flee the country when her young husband was implicated, well-wishers wrote her letters describing her young husband as a hero for silencing the Long regime. Some even sent bills in the envelopes, encouraging her to move on with her life, and some even suggested a memorial be built in her late husband's honor, but Yvonne's father made sure that all of the money was returned. To him, Judge Pavy, this tragedy bore deeply as many claimed the motive was his young son-in-law's desire to make sure Huey Long did not make this esteemed judge lose his job on the bench. Not only did he lose a son-in-law but also his beautiful, talented daughter escaped to a new country to leave behind the bitterness and danger that she felt at home. For those to whom Huey was a hero, my grandfather was a villain. There were death threats on the life of his remaining infant son, who was his father's namesake. Yvonne's decision to take her infant son and travel to France left an already-shattered family distraught. The decision for a young widow and an infant to leave the country in the 1930s was bold and fraught with the unknown, yet it was the only way she could find anonymity and safety for herself and her son, whose namesake was now an alleged assassin.

My grandmother spoke French, so France was to be her new homeland, and a swift departure ensued. The young widow needed to leave her home where there were so many signs of the man whose death turned her family name so notorious. She packed a bag, took a bus to New York, and traveled across the Atlantic Ocean to a new continent to escape the pain of the death of her husband and try to wipe the memories away. Her sisters and brothers begged her to stay, especially her younger sister Marie, to whom her beautiful older sister meant the world. The excitement of being an aunt to the firstborn nephew was quickly replaced by the void her favorite sister left. The newspapers exclaimed that young Dr. Carl Austin Weiss had killed the Kingfish. The death of a man she never knew turned her life into a tragic story and forced her to leave her comfortable home and high-profile life in search of anonymity. Aunt Marie wept for what she had lost when Yvonne and baby Carl sailed boat to France out of her life.

In a letter dated Friday May 26, 1939, Yvonne wrote:

> My dear Mother, Father, Sisters, and Brothers,
>
> "The moon is shining brightly, the music is quite restful, and Carlchen is sound asleep, so I feel free to start a detailed letter to you. I tried to be very brave when I left you, but no one will ever know how my very insides were trembling. I love all of you, and was so happy with you that it took more courage than you would give me credit for having to end it when it would have been so much easier to stay on and on with you, however, that so far everything has been perfect."

Monday May 14th, 1951.

Dear Marie,

I just got your last letter from my Mother (dated 'Tuesday'),and the contents utterly shocked me. You have several misconceptions which I would like to clear up.

Admittedly,my grades have been bad;I would never deny that. But that should not make you worry,but rather hope for me to improve,for I know you are praying. Furthermore,the last bad grade which I recorded was at the beginning of the semester. Where I got a 'D' last semester,my average this semester is very near an 'A',and if I do very well on the final,I will surely get an A. Where I got 65 in German last semester,my class average is over 90,and I have gotten over 95 on the last four tests. I am not doing well in Greek,but three weeks remain 'till the final,and I have no other tests forthcoming,so I have already started studying. I am,frankly,quite encouraged,and I am confident that if I can put forth a reasonably steady effort in my Sophomore year,all the evils performed during my Freshman year will have been corrected and made up for,and I will be on a new road,as I feel that I am now. And my age has not influenced my marks in the least.The solution is merely more work,and I have found,in the past few weeks,that the result of a little added work is immediately seen and felt.

And as for your having nothing to offer me, you have everything to offer me.The East holds nothing for me. Does going to N.Y. hold any charm for me? I would,with no offense to my Mother or Hap, just as soon live in a Pennsylvania coal-mining town,or run a hamburger stand in Death Valley, as live in N.Y.,or anywhere in the East,for that matter. There is nothing that makes me happier than the prospect of 'Home',come June 7th! And as for your getting the idea of my living in our home out of your head,that

Carl, now a toddler, and Yvonne lived a simple life in France. Yvonne got a job as a receptionist, and young Carl spent his years being loved and cared for by his courageous mother. While in

France they received letters from home. Many of the letters were from strangers with messages like, "Please take your young son and be safe. We believe in you," as one woman wrote. Some sent money to help her start a new life. Most were sympathetic, but not all. After the Kingfish died, there were death threats. Life in France was uneventful and short-lived, as World War II was imminent, and Yvonne was eager to get back to the States and start anew. She considered the move to France temporary. It was a place to gather herself and think about starting fresh. She knew eventually it was time to get back to the safety of America before a full-fledged war prevented them from safely returning. After two years in France and as World War II loomed closer, Yvonne and her small child got the last boat out of France back to America, the place he had left as a baby, an infant in exile. Yvonne and Carl Jr. were on a boat back to America as he was nearing his fifth birthday and just as the war was gearing up. Young Carl often told stories of the last boat and his return to the country of birth that he had no knowledge of. There were stories of torpedoes landing on a neighboring boat, killing all aboard. He and his mother were lucky to make it back alive as war loomed and tensions were high. Gas masks were worn aboard the boat, and torpedo drills had taken place, but this was all good practice for a life back in the United States, where surely not all had forgotten about the assassination of the man who had once been seen as a presidential contender. Going back to Louisiana was not in the cards even as they tried. They attempted it first, but Yvonne was then a hopeless expatriate from her native state. Denied the Bois de Boulogne, she took an apartment at 23 E. 76th Street, a seven-story building, living on the fourth floor. The duo settled in a new city, striking

it out in the heart of Manhattan Island, surrounded by the anonymity of millions of people far from the South, far from plantation life, and far from family. Hopefully far enough away from the
Mason-Dixon Line and those who knew their story, Yvonne and
her young son could start anew.

Six

Starting Over

Yvonne and my father in New York 1944

AFTER YVONNE AND her rambunctious son landed safely on the shores of Ellis Island, they began a new life in New York. My father was now old enough to write in journals, and he would switch his writings between French and English. He kept extensive writings in black-and-white composition books, and it was said that his mother held on to his things as if they were bound for a museum. Even as a young boy, my father was more astute than other boys his age, and he often called his mother by her first name. My father was more of a miniature man than a child, and while his mother worked long hours, he would take care of himself and travel through the city alone.

To her family Yvonne was called "a bit bohemian" and not at all as conservative and careful as she was raised. Living and working in a city as diverse as New York City in the 1940s as a single mother was an eyebrow raiser, and her family wanted her home. They visited and Yvonne acquiesced to their will, putting religious pictures on the wall in anticipation of visits by her more pious southern sisters. But it is clear from the diplomas she earned and dissertations she wrote that her objectives in New York were largely scholarly. She enrolled in Columbia University and attended school in the evenings when she should have been home caring for her growing boy.

Summers, though, were what my father lived for. Once school finished, the last week of May, he and his mother would board the Southerner, a coach train that left Penn Station at 1:30 or 2:00 p.m., to arrive in New Orleans the next night at 6:00 or 7:00 p.m. My father knew every stop on the route and remembered the loud clickety-clack of the rails clearly, as the welded track came along years later, and with that went a sound that railroad buffs can still hear and feel. The dining car was the highlight of the trip, since it afforded travelers a respite. You could read only so long. The seats, of course, did not recline all the way, and there were no Pullman bunks to sleep in. The return trip was always a fairly somber affair—it meant leaving the support of a large family setting, access to farm life, pets, and summertime friends for a lot of school and the rather dreary life in NYC. Yvonne and my father made the round trip twenty times during those years. The fare stayed about eighty dollars round trip.

My father's most memorable trip was in 1943, when he

was eight years old and set out to make the trip by himself. He brought a small white bag—marbles might have come in it—with a drawstring tied to one of the belt loops on his left side, and he was provided with small change for eating. Yvonne left him in the care of the hostess (as there were such people on the train in the 1940s), and this woman agreed to watch him closely. During subsequent summer travels and as he got older (older than eight), Yvonne would deposit her son on the southbound train and instruct him to befriend a uniformed military person. It was her belief that anyone in uniform was trustworthy and would be a great companion for a child traveling alone. Yvonne thought nothing of these solo travels for a young boy, which were a two-day affair. Her family, though, was horrified when they retrieved him from the station alone, telling stories of the service man he had befriended or the game of chicken he had played—he would exit the train at each station and jump back to safety when the train would begin to roll to avoid being stranded in a strange town.

Yvonne's younger sister, Ida, took the opportunity to move to New York at the urging of her family to help her sister manage working, mothering, and going to school. Ida enrolled in Katharine Gibbs School, and the two sisters tag-teamed rearing my father. Ida became a second mother but more like a sister to him as she was just eleven years older than my father. It was one of the best years of his childhood, for now he had two mothers. That was the year Yvonne busily prepared her only son for an audition on Quiz Kids, a popular television game show for gifted students to test their knowledge. She felt that he was brilliant, as most mothers do, but he did have an extremely high IQ, so he was chosen to compete on the radio quiz program. He was beat out by Joel Kupperman, who went on to become a national sensation and a household name, especially in our house. My mother mentioned Joel Kupperman from time to time when my father needed to be reminded that he was not the smartest man around. My mother had a tendency to resent my father's childhood, with all of the doting aunts and uncles who made him the center of their universe during those hot summers in Louisiana. Many times this kind of child-rearing made him an impossible adult to be married to, according to my mother. But Aunt Ida would not stay long and yearned to be back in Louisiana, while Yvonne stayed in New York.

Yvonne still made short visits to her sleepy hometown, Opelousas, in south-central Louisiana, always inspiring some wonder among Yvonne's peers as well. She traveled easily abroad, where New Orleans or Galveston were the outer limits for them. My father remembered that his mother worried little about money and spent it while available, although she laughed about being "land poor" (an idea easily understood in the Old South). She was truly fashionable and wore large, colorful hats or veils when they were in vogue. She never really minded making a splash. All the while, her family longed for her to return home, but Yvonne wanted to establish a world where her son would not carry the name of an assassin with him into all he did. She needed a place where she could raise her son without a cloud of suspicion. While Louisiana still reeled from the death of Huey Long, Yvonne had moved on. Besides, how could she possibly survive in a state where the Long family still dominated the political landscape? How could a child who bore the name of a man who had been found guilty of killing the Kingfish ever have a chance in Louisiana? The funeral of Huey Long was attended by thirty thousand mourners. His "Every Man a King" resonated with the rural poor for whom he gave the hope that he would lift them up out of poverty. He was a sort of modern-day Robin Hood, yet Huey Long amassed his own wealth too by lining his pockets and those of his cronies. This was certainly not a safe place for a young boy named Carl Austin Weiss Jr., so the hustle and bustle of New York City kept them safe and unknown.

The trips to Louisiana and back proceeded and came to be my father's most concrete measure of time—NYC to New Orleans the last week of May, a long summer filled with a new adventure, it seemed, almost every day. He went from New Orleans back to NYC the third week of September and the same round trip virtually every December to spend Christmas in Louisiana. He made the trip with cousins and aunts at times, and sometimes with his mother, but often alone. Somehow, the Southerner was an important element of his New York, one that linked "home" in Louisiana with the somewhat more alien world in NYC. In Opelousas he was treated like a small king in some sort of effort to wipe away the darkness of his family legacy, of the sorrow and shame that they all felt. His father's family, while close by in New Orleans, did not play a prominent role. It was as if all of the adults wanted to wipe that dark day in history out of the life of the boy whom they loved so much. They wanted him to be a carefree Louisiana boy, even if just for the summer. For him, New York was duty; Louisiana was everything else.

Back in New York, he was an only child living with his single mother in a quiet neighborhood in Manhattan. Carl reveled in the attention of his southern family, but he had grown into a pudgy city boy with horn-rimmed glasses and a pale urban complexion. He was a fine student with a quirky brilliance who attended a French lycée where all of his studies were in French. It was the fall of 1942, and he was then seven years old, though his classmates were a bit older. They were a confusing babble of divergent backgrounds ranging from a few Americans whose parents were determined they should have a European schooling to Africans from Morocco or Algeria, Russians, Central Europeans, French people, Brits, and South Americans. The school was quite serious to the point of being austere about education. French was definitely not a foreign tongue, and his first foreign language elective could have been English. Instead he chose Spanish, which he felt seemed easier.

While his Opelousas family was planting soybeans and eating large midday meals in the country, his days as a student at the lycée were serious and only interrupted by reluctant attendance at gym in a truly unusual setting. The floor was black-and-white marble, the walls were mirrored from floor to ceiling, and the gym uniform consisted of putting on a pair of sneakers and leaving street shoes in the classroom desks. They jumped rope or formed circles; there was no room for soccer, and there certainly were no basketball hoops or other nods to American culture. He was a child living in two very different and very unusual worlds.

When he was six or seven years old, his mother would ship him south on the Southerner, where his aunt Marie and uncle Veazie always met him. He made the trip alone but carried his dog, a dachshund named Liza Jane (they were all called Liza Jane) in a carrying case, and his mother told him not to talk to strangers. That was a simple request back in simpler times, and simply saying it was almost enough.

Once in the country, this fatherless boy had male cousins and uncles who taught him the ways of southern country life. He stripped off his white shirts and hard-soled shoes and replaced them with dungarees and T-shirts for bird hunting and fishing, horseback riding, and shearing sheep. This was the place where my father reverted back to a country boy in his boyhood home, though he only spent summers on Cherry Street. He was the little prince, and my mother found the doting impossible to take while my father fell back in time into the bosom of the Pavy family.

SEVEN

A "Firearms Accident"

My Dad and Snowflake in the Country

As a TWELVE-YEAR-OLD living in New York, this boyish king learned about his father's infamy while reading an issue of *LIFE* magazine that published the now-famous depiction of the shooting in the capitol. Until then young Carl had been told only that his father died in a "firearms accident." But somehow he stumbled upon a *LIFE* magazine picture of the scene at the capitol of Huey Long running from the fray while bodyguards fired shots from every direction into the frail body of a young bespectacled man. The mystery of his father's death by firearms and the discovery of the *LIFE* magazine cover meant that his mother had some explaining to do. She had long kept her young son out of the limelight, away from the fray and the repercussions of his forefathers, yet this was a setback. Even though he traveled to Louisiana every summer to frolic with cousins and family, this event had been shrouded in secrecy. All who knew were sworn to silence, and Yvonne may have thought she could get away with it forever. It was as if the mere sight of my father would command the family to stand at attention and treat him with kid gloves. His presence in Louisiana for those summers was supposed to be an indoctrination into what his life might have been if not for the event. When my father was present in the state of his birth, he was to be schooled in all things Cajun and learn everything from food to customs so as to be a real Cajun despite his home being in Yankee territory, which was another tragedy the family had to overcome. My father never spoke of the new information that his father was named as a murderer. He kept this dark secret to himself; this was not the era of therapy and self-esteem building, it was a time of grit and self-reliance, and my grandmother was not one for shedding tears. History would repeat itself, and this story was deeply buried and not dug up for many years.

Despite the family history of gun violence, my father took up hunting and became an expert marksman under the tutelage of a father figure named A. K., short for Alan Key, with whom he spent summers. A. K. was an old family friend who wanted to see that the only Pavy progeny got a suitable education about the Louisiana woodlands. He wanted to take the city out of the boy and educate him in the proper ways to be a country kid. During summer visits A. K. took Carl on fishing and hunting trips into the woods, and it was A. K. who showed this fatherless boy how to hunt turkeys and taught him about birds and dogs. This skill would later prove problematic on a trip to survey some hunting grounds when a plane went down with a young pilot at the helm.

EIGHT

Landed Gentry

Pictured in The Opelousas Daily World Circa 1973

YEARS LATER, AFTER being educated at the French lycée in New York, attending the College of the Holy Cross in Worcester, Massachusetts, and completing his medical education at Columbia University in Manhattan, the South had taken a back seat to his life as a doctor on Long Island. Now, except for the occasional trip to see family, he had settled down with a wife, with roots in New York and friends who were like family. So whenever my father arrived in Opelousas with his young family, he was treated like landed gentry. As soon as he set foot on Louisiana earth, his accent thickened, and my mother would roll her eyes at the sound of "Y'all." We'd spend a week on the farm among families whom we knew only one week a year, but our grandfather's death left us all indelibly printed in the hearts and minds of the townspeople of the Opelousas. The pictures in the paper each year of us sitting atop a rock in front of the *Opelousas Daily* meant nothing to us, but now I realize that those who lived during the tumultuous time of Huey Long deemed our grandfather a hero and wanted to know what had become of us. Rarely did we wonder why the photo of my sister Christina, brother Carl III, and me made the front page with the caption, "Carl Austin Weiss and family visit the Pavy family on Cherry Street." Our aunt Marie paraded us through the streets of Opelousas, proudly introducing and reintroducing us from year to year as "Carl's children, from New Yawk," in her thick southern accent. Their eyes would widen, and they'd pay more attention to us than we wanted, but it was the same from year to year. The townspeople watched us grow, and it was important for them to pay homage to the survivors of Carl Austin Weiss, the man who was either directly or indirectly responsible for taking down a political dynasty. The Long family held steadfastly to the idea that my grandfather was a murderer. In the small town of Opelousas, Louisiana, most believed that he was innocent. But when we came to town, all came out to see the family of that poor doctor killed by the Long regime.

My mother tried to escape the attention and rushed to the Palace Cafe for a plate of her favorite dish, Pete's fried chicken salad. There were so many things about the South that we loved and things that were found nowhere else. We ate crawfish étouf-fée, drank Cokes made with high-fructose corn syrup from green-glass bottles, and enjoyed Piggly Wiggly–brand saltines with deviled ham from Aunt Marie's pantry. Her pantry fascinated me. There were thin shelves of rustic pine, covered with red-and-white plaid contact paper. Aunt Marie loved red, and her kitchen was her favorite red place. Saltines in a red-tin box and other food that had outgrown its expiration date were perched atop the shelves. It was food I had never seen before; it was dated and dusty, and even though I was a picky eater, everything at Marie's was a treat to me. The country was a coveted and far-off place that we loved to visit. We were in awe of small-town life, despite our notoriety.

My mother, Mary Jane, loved and revered Aunt Marie. While she held the rest of the southern crowd at arm's length, she would do anything for her aunt Marie and vice versa. My mother was strong and opinionated. You either loved her or got out of her way, and in this world of southern charm, she was often mistaken as cold and unfiltered. But Marie was the one person in her husband's world who saw without judgment my mother who came from a small, nondescript family in Brooklyn. She took my mother in and was one of the few people in my father's world to really welcome her into the fold. They remained steadfast friends throughout their lives.

When my father first took his new wife, my mother, to the South to meet the family, she was subjected by a doting family to story after story of every move made by her new husband. My mother would tell us years later in an irked and unimpressed tone of voice that they reported on his first bowel movement. She rarely tried to cap her resentment and was an eye-rolling aficionado who cared little of what others thought. My mother was adopted from an orphanage in New York City, and while she lamented her lack of family, she spoke of her early days in the New York Foundling as if it were a finishing school for toddlers. My mother was considered a cold New Yorker who was not equipped with southern charm, an outsider, and one without lineage to boot. It made her seem fiercer, and she felt that she had to be tough. She was adopted at four and was said to have spoken Italian when my grandparents, John and Ann, adopted her. My grandfather was an uneducated man with a tattoo on his arm from his early days as a boxer. Back in those days, tattoos were a reflection of masculinity and bad boys. Those from the other side of the tracks were more likely to have them. My grandfather, along with his brother, owned a floral and curio shop in Brooklyn. My grandmother never took pictures of Mary Jane for fear that someone would recognize her in the picture and take her back. In one of the few early pictures of my mother, she is standing in front of a fountain wearing a navy cape and holding a doll. She grew up to look and dress like Jackie Kennedy, despite her humble beginnings. While many did not understand her, they were in awe of this city girl who had captured the heart of the brilliant doctor and had kept him in New York, far away from his boyhood home in southern Louisiana.

NINE

The Doctor Is In

My Mom and Dad as Rhett Butler and Scarlet O'Hara 1980

And their wedding in 1961

MY PARENTS MET when my mother was a scrub nurse in the emergency room at Bellevue Hospital in the Bronx, and my father was in his last year of residency on a path to be an orthopedic surgeon.

My mother was a beautiful brunette with deep brown eyes and had been engaged to the chief of surgery before breaking off that engagement due to a large age gap. My mother talked about her first love often, despite my father not noticing her desire to make him jealous. It took a lot to get my father's attention. He was usually consumed with himself, as a doted-on only child; he cared little for outside distractions, and the conversations were usually about him. My mother was along for the ride, and her resentment of his larger-than-life presence stood at the forefront of my childhood.

As the wife of a prominent orthopedic surgeon in an affluent New York suburb, she took her role in the community very seriously. She was the chairwoman of the American Cancer Society and hosted lavish parties on the lawn of the sprawling three-story colonial she and my father owned. It was a house of prominence for a lady who always believed she was bound for greatness. She wore large diamond earrings bought in the costume jewelry section at Saks Fifth Avenue down the street and once told me, "When I wear them, everyone thinks they are real." She carried herself with a convincing aristocratic air that no one dared challenge her on. In her element in New York, she made a life for her family due to her persistence and love of all things beautiful and my father's fifty-hour workweek that brought him home late at night and had him leaving early every morning. He was a master in the operating room and ran a busy orthopedic medical practice so that my mother could decorate our large home with expensive wallpaper from Schumacher and cover couches and chairs with fabric from the best interior design houses in Manhattan. She had given up nursing to go to interior design school at the reputable Parsons School as soon as we were old enough to need her less. She threw cocktail and dinner parties that everyone wanted an invitation to. One year my mother saw a costume of Scarlett O'Hara and decided that she needed to wear it, so she planned a Halloween party so that she could walk down the staircase in our house. She had a striking resemblance to the character, and on the night of the party, she traipsed down the long spiral staircase just as Scarlett O'Hara did in an antebellum gown with ruffles from head to toe in the famous scene in *Gone With the Wind*, while sixty or seventy guests watched the scene unfold from their own colorful costumes. Of course my father waited at the bottom of the steps dressed as Rhett Butler. The party was such a success that it was talked about for years, just as my mother had hoped.

My mother loved to be the center of attention, as did my father, and they were forever in each other's crosshairs. Ultimately my father would give in and go to the golf course or the operating room, where he was always king of his domain because he demanded it. And he was respected by friends and colleagues for his intellect and confidence. My siblings and I cannot count the number of times that our friends, our friends' parents, and people we did not know told us how much they liked "Doc Weiss." He was the town doctor, and everyone had an arm set, a skin disorder diagnosed, an ankle wrapped with an ACE bandage, or a prescription written by my father. He gave medical advice to anyone who asked. He even did house calls whenever anyone asked. On weekends, instead of going to the emergency room, if someone sprained an ankle or even broke a bone roughhousing or playing in a town recreation league, they always called my father first, and they would show up at the house for a first opinion. This habit of seeing patients at home, at others' homes, and at odd hours was a constant source of strife for my mother. She thought it distasteful and inappropriate for my father to do house calls; she hated the idea of others taking advantage. My father often examined patients in makeshift examining rooms wherever he happened to be—the changing room of the golf clubs he belonged to, wide spots in hallways, or even in the dining rooms of restaurants where he and my mother were eating. My mother did not just resent this because she hated for him to be taken advantage of, but his ego was often not in check as well. This reverence from the community made him even harder to live with, or so she thought.

And so on trips to the country, the combination of his ego as an orthopedic surgeon and as the son of Louisiana made him especially intolerable. It was on those trips my mother was forced to take a back seat. She did it through clenched teeth while the family doted on my father. This place, our father's boyhood home, held a fascination for all but my mother. For her it was that dreaded trip to the in-laws', but we suburban kids drenched ourselves in local color and thought that this way of life was seemingly normal. The large and raucous midday feasts, the rows of soybean fields on horseback, and the family storytelling times on the back porch happened like routine but for just a week a year.

TEN

Aunt Marie

My Mom and Marie in her kitchen

MY MOTHER LOVED Aunt Marie for many reasons. She had a heart of gold and was known to all in the town. Marie tried to leave Opelousas, trying her hand at college, but retreated to the place where time stood still—her home on Cherry Street. After short stints away, she returned home and remained until her death at eighty-seven of old age. It was the same story for her sister Evelyn and brother Bebe, who never even tried to leave but carried out their lives in the home where they were born and reared. They were spinsters and were regarded as such by the neighbors and anyone who knew the family. Aunt Marie was the gregarious one and the one who was revered by the

47

townsfolk. She had a loud, infectious laugh and was forever telling stories. She never let the truth stand in the way of a good story, though she never lied—she remembered things grandly. Strangers loved Marie, but her family of nieces and nephews and great-nieces and great-nephews adored her. It is said that an aunt or uncle can take more liberties than a father or mother, and all who knew Marie called her Miss Marie or Aunt Marie with a fondness that made me jealous. I wanted her to be all mine, but in a small town like Opelousas, everyone had a connection to her and a connection to the event that changed the town of Opelousas many years before. The story of my grandfather's death belonged to everyone who knew him. Being the birthplace of Carl Austin Weiss's widow was the only notoriety a town like Opelousas would ever have.

It is hard to remember when I realized how lucky I was to have Aunt Marie. Maybe the peculiarity of my southern heritage dawned on me while listening to family and friends step up to the pulpit of St. Landry Church to remember the woman everyone called "Aunt Marie." The eulogy given by my father, her favorite nephew, brought the assembled family and countless friends to laughter and tears simultaneously. There were stories of her super fandom of the LSU football team, where Aunt Marie religiously attended the football games and traveled by bus with her cousin Coy on the hour-long trek to Tiger Stadium in Baton Rouge. She rarely knew the name of the opposing team or the score at the end but just came simply for the halftime show. If her loyalty to the game of football came into question, never would one question her allegiance to the home team as she donned team colors, a tawdry combination of mustard yellow and amethyst purple. Her cheers for the home team were those of pure joy at watching the boys, some of which were "her boys," as she'd taught many of them at Opelousas High.

There were times when Aunt Marie traveled to New York to see her favorite nephew, my father, and his family. New York might just as well have been France. And while Carl visited his southern roots every summer and immersed himself in the culture of Opelousas, he was raised a northerner, a Yankee, north of the Mason-Dixon Line. He was a "New York" doctor, and the pride they felt was as strong as the loss they felt that he lived so far off in such a strange land.

The preparations for the annual visit from Aunt Marie meant planning her city wardrobe and telling everyone in town about the long journey north to the Big Apple to visit her favorite nephew, the doctor. There were new clothes with matching purses to purchase and tickets for Broadway musicals to buy. My mother did the shopping. She was a city girl and knew that her husband's aunt and her favorite in-law was in need of a fashion boost. She shopped at the local Lane Bryant and bought Aunt Marie several coordinating outfits that Marie would rave about and tell all who would listen that her new duds were a gift from her favorite niece in New York. My mother was a staunch proponent of the right clothing, and not just her own. One year when my father's cousin—named Octave, or "eight," as he was the eighth born—visited, he traveled to Manhattan to see a Broadway musical wearing a one-piece jumpsuit, the ones worn by auto mechanics working under the hood of a car. Stylish southerners they were not, and my mother turned her nose up at many of the fashion faux pas my father's family was known for; they were from the rural South, after all.

Most of Marie's preparations to leave Opelousas for a trip to the Big Apple consisted of finding someone to look after the farm and take care of the remaining siblings, who were just too "country" for this kind of journey. Aunt Marie took this trip once a year and would captivate the friends of her nephew with one of her inextricably southern terms like, "You're story-ing me," a euphemism that meant the tale sounded exaggerated or downright false. All who met her for any amount of time recalled her southern charm and genuineness with certain dis-belief that she was so real, so delightful. Marie left a wake of smiles with her downright southern charm. In New York Marie fascinated those in the big city who did not know that her kind of naiveté still existed. She told everyone that she was Carl's old aunt. Even if they did not know Carl, she told them stories of her nephew, the doctor, with such pride that his status was im-mediately elevated by her awe of him. Here in the suburbs of New York, only my father's close friends knew of his father's death and the unsolved whodunit. Aunt Marie was just one of the cast of characters from his upbringing and each time she visited us, she left a mark on all who met her. Everyone wanted an Aunt Marie.

ELEVEN

A Red Lady

ANYONE WHO KNEW Aunt Marie knew that she wore red, loved red, and was buried in a coffin adorned with big red roses. She wore red shoes, carried bright-red purses, tied a long red scarf under her chin, and applied red lipstick to her slightly too-powdered face—a graceful, enduring red. She called herself a "red lady."

She was a fixture in the rural town that had been the capital of the Confederacy for a short time during the Civil War. Her father's mahogany bed was stripped of its tester to be used as a tablecloth for an impromptu meal for a political campaign. Aunt Marie referred to it as the "Silver War" because of the silver flatware set neatly tucked away in her buffet, monogrammed with a W for Wartelle, the original occupants of the home. During the war, the

Wartelle family was forced to bury their valuables under the large oak tree that stood in the front yard, for fear of them being stolen by Yankee soldiers. Years later the silver was found under the oak tree by Judge Pavy, Aunt Marie's "papa," as she called him. That silverware was proudly set on the breakfront to be used whenever the family gathered in the dining room for the midday meal. The "Silver War" was a time in history when everyone feared for the safety of the family silver, according to Aunt Marie.

Her father, the judge, was so admired and respected that streets were named in his honor in the small town where generations of Pavys raised their families. The Pavys were a southern family—seven children were born to the judge, called this because of his long-standing post as the judge of St. Landry Parish. Aunt Marie was the fourth in line, born in "Papa's bed," the name for the maple four-poster canopied bed that occupied the front room. Marie was the colorful one who never liked to be far from home. Twice she traveled to college and came home to the only home she would ever know, where the oak tree greeted her. Each time she returned home, her parents would pack her bags and send Marie back to Louisiana State University, but she hated being away from home. Eventually Aunt Marie finished college. She got her first job teaching Louisiana history. It was common knowledge that Marie taught her own version of Louisiana history, and there was no mention of Huey Long as the great son of the state and certainly no mention of her late brother-in-law as the assassin. No one dared question Miss Marie; she taught three decades of students, and they loved her despite her history lessons skipping large swaths of information during the Louisiana history chapters.

After the tragic death of her brother-in-law and his supposed involvement in the death of Louisiana's governor, life changed for Aunt Marie. So when Papa died and her mother was gone, she moved back into the old family house to keep the traditions of her childhood alive. Entry into the inner yard of the property was gained through the gateway of a whitewashed picket fence with an arched walkway where yellow roses wove their way through the latticed woodwork for a springtime show. On either side of the gateway were settees, which beckoned during the leisurely visits of all who entered, as did the swing on the screened-in front porch, where all who visited gathered.

The remaining three siblings lived together on Cherry Street until their deaths. Marie lived alone on the rambling plantation well into her eighties, when it was decided that she could no longer care for the house herself. She devoted most of her days to preserving life on Cherry Street just as it had always been, maintaining the same furniture upholstered in velvets and floral patterns chosen by her mother. The Pavy home was furnished with antiques and family treasures, the date of which reflected the many stages and additions to the home. Remarkable examples of bisque china are noted on mantels throughout the house, and cloths of fine handwork and cutwork grace the antique tabletops. In the living room were a garniture French clock with inlaid brass and old French vases set in domes, which were brought over from France by Eugene Wartelle's father, Pierre, when he left France to make plans for Napoleon to come to Louisiana. This may well be where my grandmother's connection to France was born.

TWELVE

Yvonne Passes On

AT MARIE'S HOME in the country, we only shared family stories that made us laugh. When we visited our father's boyhood home, we, too, never talked about the death of his father, and as children we did not know any details of the event. Our older cousins, though, had studied Louisiana history (the real version, not Aunt Marie's made-up version where Huey Long was never mentioned). On the porch under the whirling fan, we'd sit on the lopsided daybed or one of the wicker chairs—this is where we'd gather for informal laughing and "carrying on," as my mother called it. Anyone who had dropped by for the day would sip a cold drink from Aunt Marie's collection of red barware. The country was a place where everyone had time for one another, and only the good memories were remembered.

So while in the entire state of Louisiana the death of Huey Long was embedded in their lives as seen on street signs, bridges, and in the statewide education system, for us Yankee kids, this event and our attachment to it were veritable secrets. We knew the country as a jolly place of family stories, except the one that was buried in a deep hole in the backyard. The despair that pervaded this plantation home around the time of "the event" must have been like an albatross around the necks of anyone related to my grandfather living in the South, which was half of Opelousas and a small part of New Orleans. The brothers and sisters were devastated by the loss of innocence and the once-powerful Judge Pavy weakened and defeated. Yet with time the Pavy family was determined to change this situation for the better. Silence and their version of history were the weapons to fight the sorrowful event that left the only progeny fatherless until his aunt Ida gave birth to his first cousin, Henry. For so long he was the sole heir of the Pavy legacy and was so revered that he took on godlike qualities. He was the child who would never know his father, and his mother, Yvonne, would die of cancer just after the birth of her first grandchild, when her son, Carl, was just thirty.

The marriage to my mother had not been a welcome event to my father's protective family and had actually been boycotted altogether by them. My grandmother Yvonne had not been so keen on her only son marrying the daughter of a homemaker and a curio shop owner from Brooklyn. It was not the lineage she saw for her son, and she was a northerner to boot. She even went so far as to shun her only child's wedding. The prodigal son was married in a small ceremony in Brooklyn, attended only by my mother's very small family with no representation by Yvonne or her family.

This is another of those stories that was supposed to be left alone as per my mother. The embarrassment that she was not accepted by my father's side of the family loomed large for her, so much so that this absence of family at her wedding was a taboo subject. We learned that my mother's lineage was not acceptable to his mother, as she was adopted and reared in Brooklyn to a couple that were themselves ordinary New Yorkers. Owning a floral and curio shop was not considered respectable enough, and perhaps they knew that John had a tattoo, though I doubt it.

I credit my love of flower arranging to my grandfather and tell anyone who will listen that my grandfather was a florist, yet this match was considered beneath my father, Dr. Carl Austin Weiss Jr., a Columbia University Medical School graduate and the fourth Weiss in the family to become a doctor. This rift continued for years until the birth of my sister in 1965, when eventually and reluctantly, my grandmother gave her only daughter-in-law a chance.

The young couple was even living in Louisiana while my father was stationed at Barksdale Air Force Base in Shreveport. Choosing to fulfill their mandatory service in the South was a gesture by my mother to get to know the other side of the family. My young parents lived in Bossier City, sister city to Shreveport, in a neighborhood called Shady Grove, which my mother often referred to as "Shady Grave," either due to the excessive heat she endured in the summers or the fact that it was a far cry from the bustle of New York, and she feared she might die there. My mother both delighted in and hated living in the South. She remembered her days spending time with the other wives at the Officers Club and made many good friends there but would not stay there long, and my brother and I were both born in New York. My parents eventually settled on Long Island in the home that Yvonne bought in a comfortable suburb a short train ride from Manhattan. Yvonne was diagnosed with colon cancer; it was a shocking blow as my mother had just forged a relationship with her mother-in-law.

Yvonne was married to a man who was much older, but she was just fifty-four and a new grandmother. She had waited a long time to marry again, almost thirteen years, to a man who had lost his wife and had just one child. Ironically, Mimi, Hap's only daughter, had nine children with her husband Bill. So young Carl went from being the only feature in his mother's life to a boy with an older stepfather and nine step-nieces and step-nephews. My mother recalled the scene of visiting the large brood of Mimi and Bill's children, some in footie pajamas, others in diapers, and an assembly line of pea-nut-butter-and-jelly sandwich making in the kitchen. That Yvonne went from a young widow with one child to a married woman with twelve step-grandchildren was a testament to the man she chose. Hap was his name, and they were happily married for eighteen years when she was diagnosed with colon cancer at age fifty-three. Colon cancer was a death sentence in those days, and little could be done. Her marriage to Hap had been one of the few times of peace and comfort in her otherwise turbulent life.

So sudden was her tragic and untimely diagnosis that her sickness rendered her unable to complete her doctoral degree in romance languages, a rarity for a woman in the 1940s, yet it was conferred posthumously in 2016. She was returned to Louisiana to be buried next to her husband in the family plot at the St. Landry Parish, the Romanesque revival church where Aunt Marie celebrated Mass every Sunday, just down the street from their childhood home.

Yvonne died the same year that a new grandchild, Carl Austin, was born prematurely and died at three days old. Both are buried in the Opelousas cemetery, and my brother, who was born a year later and named Carl Austin, never liked visiting the family plot and seeing his name on the little boy's tombstone. It was a matter-of-fact visit to the cemetery where everyone talked in hushed voices, just another story that was never told. Maybe they assumed we knew the history, but I just thought my father was larger than life anyway; I knew nothing of the past.

My father's childhood was like that—a long volley of stories that had no endings, only colorful beginnings and peculiar middles, and we heard them all. My father's boyhood hometown was a magical place where telling stories was the main activity, sitting together with generations of family was expected, and the pictures on the wall were of all of us. The front parlor of Marie's house was where we gathered to tell stories.

Family Tree

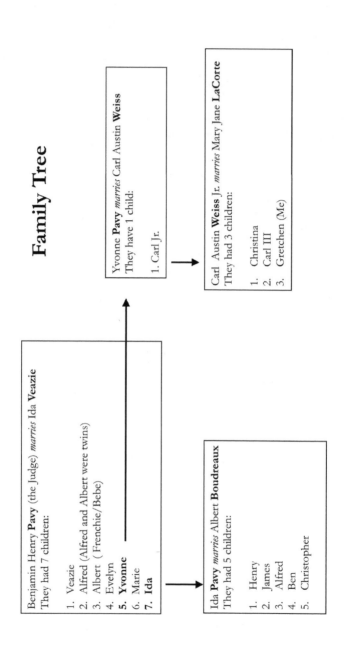

Benjamin Henry **Pavy** (the Judge) *marries* Ida **Veazie**
They had 7 children:

1. Veazie
2. Alfred (Alfred and Albert were twins)
3. Albert (Frenchie/Bebe)
4. Evelyn
5. **Yvonne**
6. Marie
7. **Ida**

Yvonne **Pavy** *marries* Carl Austin **Weiss**
They have 1 child:

1. Carl Jr.

Carl Austin **Weiss** Jr. *marries* Mary Jane **LaCorte**
They had 3 children:

1. Christina
2. Carl III
3. Gretchen (Me)

Ida **Pavy** *marries* Albert **Boudreaux**
They had 5 children:

1. Henry
2. James
3. Alfred
4. Ben
5. Christopher

THIRTEEN

The Immediate Family Tree

The Pavy sisters (Marie, Yvonne, Ida, and Evelyn) Circa 1950

THE HOME WHERE the oak tree stood tall was occupied for many years. Marie, her brother, Bebe, and her sister, Evelyn, never married, and lived and died in the family home. They were a couple of spinsters and a quirky bachelor living together until their deaths of old age. Aunt Marie's brother, Veazie, the eldest son, also spent a lifetime caring for his boyhood home and everyone in it. He married late in life, never had children, and practiced law behind the sign that read "Pavy & Pavy" in the heart of Opelousas. Every day he ambled up the porch steps of his boyhood home to drop off the daily mail. "Aaaay, Marie," he'd shout from the porch in a thick Cajun accent, wearing a bolero hat and horn-rimmed glasses. The screen door would screech and slam behind him; rarely were the doors locked. It was his job to oversee his homebound siblings. He'd stay for midday dinner and head back to the small law office where he practiced for forty years until he also died of old age. Aunt Marie admired her oldest brother. He carried the torch for his parents. The siblings, all but Yvonne, lived a short drive from one another, and most days the midday meal was eaten in the childhood home at the dining room table, which was in the center of the house and overlooked every other room. The windows were still inside the house, and since Marie was not a private person, her bedroom was in the center of the house, and the windows exposed her to the parlor. She would go to bed early while family still gathered and talked, but being a sound sleeper, she was known to snore loudly, and all could hear.

Sister, as Evelyn was called, lived in the front of the house where she had her own bathroom and bedroom that had been added later to give her more privacy. The sprawling antebellum home had many additions that added modern conveniences like indoor plumbing and a stove for indoor cooking. Sister was a very private person and rarely spoke. She was gentle, awkward, and only spoke to chide her little sister Marie for her foolishness. Sister was very serious and smiled a shy, downward smile. She rarely called attention to herself. While Bebe was long thought to be a crazy man by outsiders, inside the home he was a gentle man who always wore a bathrobe and slippers to walk across the squeaky wood floors. His room was filled with LSU memorabilia and horse knickknacks. Rarely did Bebe entertain visitors in his room, but once outside the four walls, he was the center of attention, though he rarely spoke, and he was mysterious even to us. As a child I knew nothing of the death of his twin brother by suicide. I never questioned why he had never left home and had not worked a day in his life. It never seemed odd that his two older sisters cared for him. I never wondered why he was missing all of his teeth. He was our very own Mr. Magoo. It was our yearly visits that brought Bebe out of his room, out of his comfort zone, to be with his favorite nephew, my father. When he was present for that week on the farm, everyone seemed happier. They were happy that the prodigal son had returned and brought his family back to his boyhood home, back to his roots in the country where they would regale him with stories of his home. My mother prepared herself for this week of total doting, though she did not care for many of the adults. She was a northerner, and she could take the good-natured ribbing most of the time, but Aunt Marie was the one she loved—we all loved Marie.

Sister was the cook and was next in birth order. She cooked and cared for the house. Sister was a wonderful cook, yet she rarely spoke or looked you in the eye. Maybe it was because of her acne-scarred complexion that she rarely smiled. There were charcoal drawings by an aspiring young artist hanging in the hallway and a memento of art from each of Bebe's New York nieces and nephews. He was never quite capable of life on his own after the death of his twin brother. When his twin brother, Taboy, died, time stopped for Uncle Bebe. He remained in his bedroom off the west side of the home, where he would herd the cows from his porch even after the cows had been gone for ten years or more. Rarely dressed in anything but a terrycloth bathrobe, he spoke very little, only telling those who crossed the train tracks that ran parallel to his boyhood home to cross them "on the bias." These were the things that we learned in the country: the correct way to cross over the raised cattle guards and defunct railroad tracks at an angle. This decreased the wear and tear on the tires and kept the passengers from a experiencing a bumpy event. There were a few other tidbits that he'd share, but his experiences were limited to home, managing a small herd of cows, and looking over the farmers who planted soybeans on his family's acreage year after year while his brothers and sister looked after him. A gentle man with a gaunt face and soft, pale hands, he always wore a bolero hat whenever he appeared in public, which was quite seldom. He only took it off to greet a lady, yet he clutched the hat in front of him till he could put the hat back on, which seemingly cloaked him in invisibility. His discomfort with the world outside his boyhood home turned him into a bewildering character.

The neighborhood kids told stories of the crazy old man who lived in the big house and herded the long-gone cows. Dressed in his usual white terrycloth robe, a new one given to him each birthday by my mother, he'd stand on his screened-in porch and chant, "Up, up," through thin, aging lips, urging the cows to mosey along. Even as youngsters, we never questioned why Frenchie (another name we called Bebe) spent the day swaddled in his robe behind a closed door, herding imaginary cows. When my father came to town, they say Frenchie came out more, spoke more, and smiled more than he had done in the year since my father's last visit. They say it was because my father was Yvonne's son, her only child, and to love her son was to love her.

Yvonne was the second-youngest sibling, the only one brave enough to leave home, and Marie marveled at her grace and charm. When she brought home a young doctor who would become her husband, her younger sisters gushed and flirted with the handsome and well-traveled young man who had captured the heart of their smart older sister. The tragedy of her life reverberated throughout the family for years, perhaps decades. Marie had taken the death of her brother-in-law particularly hard, as she looked up to her sister. Yvonne graduated with a degree in French from H. Sophie Newcomb Memorial College, which was the women's college of Tulane University in New Orleans. Marie revered her dashing and smart brother-in-law, and once he was done with his residency in ear, nose, and throat medicine in Europe, the couple settled back home in Louisiana, close to both sides of their families. They lived in a small house in Baton Rouge where their son, Carl, was born on June 7, 1935. Carlshun (German for "Little Carl") was the firstborn of the brood of five remaining Pavy siblings. Little Carl, their fatherless nephew, was doted on by his many aunts and uncles, and when the shots rang out in the capitol and one of their own was accused, they dug their heels in even deeper and stayed close to home forever, despite being linked to a famous political assassination.

Ida was the youngest child of the Pavy brood, eleven years younger than her closest sibling. Ida married late in life and had five children—all boys who divided their time between home and across town at Marie's house, referred to as "the country," as it was situated on one of the few remaining large tracts of land. It was there that the boys rode horses, fished, entertained friends, impressed girls, and were wholly loved by Aunt Marie. They were her children once removed, and she cheered them on proudly in whatever they did. Marie always sat next to her sister, Ida, their mother, at graduations, football games, weddings, and christenings. Marie was a fixture in the boys' lives, and they loved her as they did their mother. She was a completely devoted aunt. Ida was married to Albert Boudreaux, an aspiring lawyer. As is the case when one marries the youngest daughter in a prominent family, Albert had to hold his own, but he partnered with the oldest Pavy brother, Veazie, and had a long-standing law practice in the center of town, though it was not without its difficulties. The eldest Pavy brother and the youngest son-in-law made up Pavy & Pavy, and the duo of lawyers spent most of their years writing up legal contracts and last wills and testaments. It was a small town, and rarely did anything out of the ordinary happen there. The allegations on the night of the Huey Long shooting turned the small town upside down. There were suspicions, conspiracy theories, and curiosity seekers who came to see where this drama began. The little town known for the Yambilee Festival had become infamous overnight.

My father was thirteen when the first of his cousins was born to his aunt Ida and uncle Albert. Until then, my father enjoyed the healthy amount of attention he received from doting aunts and uncles. Now there were four boys who came in fast succession. Cousin Chris was born last and was born much younger than his oldest brother, so he was no threat to my father. In fact, Chris and I are just a year apart, me being older.

Those five boy cousins were the heart and soul of Cherry Street for us city kids, and they were the only cousins we had, even though they were they were much older second cousins. And even though much older, they celebrated our arrival and taught us all of the things that we needed to know about our Louisiana family. I remember doing a report on a state of choice in the fifth grade and proudly learning how to spell Louisiana and how to pronounce it like a true southerner: "Looo-zee-anna." I had no idea during those early years that there was a deep family secret. It was hidden from us. No words were uttered that alluded to anything amiss. I had not yet studied American history. I was just happy to be in the bosom of my family.

The first cousin was fourteen years younger than my dad. Cousin Henry was married by the time I was twelve, and I served as the flower girl in his wedding. He was not one to keep coming back to his boyhood home. He may have been the one who was the least attached to the family home. He married early and left for Baton Rouge to start a life away from the family enclave. A busy accountant practice kept him away from Opelousas whenever we visited, as Easter usually coincided with tax time. Aunt Marie always excused Henry for missing this full-family reunion, but occasionally he would saunter into the house on Cherry Street where his wife and children were having dinner with the rest of the family. Sometimes he showed up; most times he didn't. There may have been a story there, but keeping the dark family secrets hidden was something that this tight-knit southern family did very well.

James was the sweetest of the five and took a back seat to his younger brother, Alfred. He was hardworking and mild mannered, the good child who let Alfred carry on and never called him out on his antics. James knew that Alfred needed that attention like he needed air and water, and he let him be the center of attention at so many family gatherings that Alfred's stories became legendary, even though James's accomplishments as a pilot were more than noteworthy. His boss was a guy named Warren Buffett who often flew but was so nondescript to the pilot and flight attendants that James remembers overhearing a flight attendant amazed when he gave tips for accruing wealth. They did not know they were being given tips by one of the richest men on earth. But James was like that, a true southern gentleman—never boastful. He became the father of three girls despite having no knowledge of rearing girls in the male-dominated family of Boudreaux boys.

Next in line was Alfred, the storyteller and exaggerator who never let the truth get in the way of a good story and went on to become a lawyer. He was forever talking about parties and pretty girls, and his southern charm got him in and out of trouble. He monopolized the conversation, and we had no choice but to listen. His stories of fraternity parties and frivolity were told over and over. Alfred reveled in having an entire family of aunts, uncles, and cousins to laugh at his jokes and indulge his place as the storyteller. His presence was large, and he wore a smile and expression like a jester, nodding and working the crowd. Eventually he would become the other half of Pavy & Pavy when the eldest Pavy brother died. Alfred carried the Pavy name and made a name for himself wherever he went. There were stories of frat houses and infidelity that spanned across his years of three failed marriages, twice to the same woman. He was a man with a large personality, bound for greatness, who lived in the apartment above the law office in Opelousas, a stone's throw from the Opelousas diner where he ate daily and touted his law accomplishments—most of which were DWI representations for nephews and frat brothers.

These five were so distinctly different from each other and from their quirky father, who raised a brood of tough boys without being at all masculine or commanding; he seemed as amazed that he fathered these boys as we all were. Ben was challenged by school and tried his hand on all of the blue-collar skills he thought might lead to a successful life. He tried installing air conditioners, crawfishing, raising cattle on the family farm, and other methods of farming, including soybeans. He was the workingman in the family, and early on it was clear that he needed more than just his good looks to try to match the wit and charm of his older brother. Ben would arrive to the midday meal from his job as a plumber's assistant or air conditioner installer. He struggled to find success while his brother Alfred exuded confidence.

Their distinctly different personalities, though, sometimes caused a clash. Chris, the youngest by eight years, was the object of his older brothers' disdain. His mother had favored him, and his older brothers chastised him for not playing football or being a tough kid. While they had all gotten into their fair share of trouble with drinking, girls, and cars, Chris excelled in academics and was a star pupil. He was the closest in age to his New York cousins, so when we visited for that week each year, he left school behind for the week to immerse himself in us and play capture the flag on horseback, dye Easter eggs, and take us to the Opelousas diner for my mother's favorite, fried chicken salad. Chris looked forward to our visit more than the others because he was pulled from school to play with his closest cousins. He played with us while his older brothers entertained us, until girls and dating changed them to strangers, and they came around less and less while we were there. But these were our kin, and the week each year spent encircled by Aunt Marie's white picket fence taught us more about life and family than all the weeks in the year.

FOURTEEN

The Accident

FEB · 63

Mom and Dad before the crash

EASTER WEEK WAS a long-awaited event and not because of the resurrection or anything remotely linked to Christianity. My love for the Easter holiday was not because of the Easter Bunny, though I loved him! It was my favorite time of the year because it was time to spend an entire week at the extended family home in south Louisiana, dubbed "the country." It was also the one time of the year when the family was loaded into my father's plane with just enough seats to fit the five of us. The plane that my father owned was a far-off possession that was rarely talked about. It was parked miles away at a private airstrip. It was my father's plane because anything that my father had that my mother hated, she took no possession of, especially the green Rolls-Royce he bought during his midlife crisis. The plane was entirely his, and Easter week was the only trip we took in the cream-colored plane decorated with a brown racing stripe. It looked old and rickety, and I hated it. In fact, it made me sick, and no amount of Dramamine could fend off the inevitable motion sickness. Perhaps my fear of flying stemmed from the fact that, as we piled into what I later learned was called the "fork-tailed doctor killer" because of its popularity with doctors whose hobbies were flying, my mother donned her headphones and was referred to as the copilot. Even at a young age, I knew my mother was no match for those instruments; she was as afraid of the multi-hour flight as I was. Nonetheless, we traveled this way for years until "the accident," as it was referred to in hushed tones.

My sister usually took the seat behind my mother, who looked mildly uncomfortable as my father called in his aircraft's identifiers to the control terminal. My brother bounced excitedly—he had a love of flying at a young age. He spent much of his youth building model airplanes and flying them in the yard. My father and brother spent hours gluing, sanding, and adding just the right decals to the remote-controlled planes. When the pair completed one, which took a few months of time spent together in the basement where there was an elaborate shop for building, we would all gather around to watch the first flight. Unfortunately they often ended in carnage. There was usually more frustration than success in the model-airplane-flying department, but this father-and-son airplane building was pure male bonding, and they rebuilt it each time it crashed. This was not the case for his actual flying career, but perhaps this was my father's way of staying connected to aviation after the accident grounded him for a few years. My father loved the attention of being the pilot in command of his own plane, and his southern family always welcomed us at the airport like we had just accomplished the first lunar landing. The accident changed all of that.

It was one Easter visit when my father, full of his own prowess, wanted to take to the skies for a scenic tour of a turkey-hunting ground. It was his desire to fly over this place where the year before he had shot his first wild turkey. This turkey was later stuffed and lived out its days perched on a wooden base in my father's home office, with the date of the kill inscribed on a gold plate. As children we revered the turkey and often showed our friends the turkey our father had shot. He was in mint condition, as he was merely wounded by the bullet, so his feathers were intact, and he was mounted and stuffed in perfect turkey condition with dark-brown feathers that we would often pet like a dog. We all knew the story of how my father had grazed the turkey, and when, like a good hunter, he knew his target had only been wounded, he trailed it until he found the dying bird and finished off the kill. The winged bird was still intact enough to carry out and bring to a taxidermist rather than eat. My father wanted to document his hunting conquests. That bird is still a coveted piece of history that now sits in my brother's office. It is still the symbol of the crash that stole the eyesight from Uncle Albert, deeply scarred the face of gentle and timid Sister (Aunt Evelyn), left his aunt Ida with a broken leg, nearly killed my mother, and took a notch out of my father's belt.

His passengers for the ride to the turkey-hunting grounds were his loyal family, who bestowed upon him a kingly loyalty save for my mother, his wife, who knew better but accompanied him on the flight just the same. She sat in the last seat back in the tail of the plane and knitted the crochet stitch that Aunt Marie taught her. It was tradition that each year they would combine efforts to make one for each relative in "their colors." Each crocheted square was tucked into a plastic bag until collectively my mother and Marie made enough squares to put together a blanket. Everyone in the family had a handmade crocheted blanket from their handiwork. As my mother hooked and wrapped the pink yarn, Aunts Ida and Evelyn sat behind the pilot seat in the second row of seats. Uncle Albert took Mother's usual position next to Dad at the instrument panel.

The flight path of the loyal passengers took them across the bayou and over the swamps to a small field where the turkeys had been seen grazing next to a small runway—a far cry from the life my father lived as a skilled and busy surgeon.

The plan that day was to land and survey the hunting grounds where the turkey had been shot. It was a sort of show-and-tell, and the passengers were willing participants in all of my father's adventures. My father made a visual of the runway and launched a large circle to prepare to land. On final approach, the scene changed suddenly, and a large herd of cows meandered into the flight path. The little plane, loaded with five passengers and dropping in altitude, was flying too low, so the pilot had to make the decision to either land the plane or abort. Pulling back at the wheel was the split-second decision, but the plane was heavily weighted down and lost elevation, careening over the tops of the trees, where it stalled and crashed. All of the passengers lost consciousness. As luck would have it, someone on the ground had seen the sputtering plane and alerted rescue personnel, who arrived at the scene almost immediately. There had been a light-but-sustained rain that day, and the emergency workers all remarked that because of the slippery surface of the trees, the plane had skimmed through the forest rather than careening straight to earth. The wetness had apparently been a savior, and while all five passengers sustained injuries, only my mother was listed in critical condition.

Tucked into the back of the plane was my mother with crochet needles in hand. She was so far in the back of the plane that the rescuers had to be instructed to go back to retrieve the last victim. She was nearly left for dead. Never a victim of guilt, my father would blame my mother's head injuries and subsequent six-week coma any time he felt she was being too "reactionary." He would claim she suffered permanent damage; I know it was me who drove her to ranting. Ida and her husband, Albert, also suffered severe injuries, though Ida was young enough to rehabilitate a severely broken leg. Albert, however, sustained permanent eye damage. Sister suffered trauma to her face, broken cheekbones, and facial lacerations that never fully disappeared. My father escaped nearly unscathed with a few misplaced ribs.

But Carlshun was still a hero in the eyes of all simply because he was Yvonne's orphaned son, and the accident was only mentioned in hushed tones without a hint of blame. My mother was the only one who held the accident as a terrible fall from grace. She spent six weeks in a coma and suffered a broken hip, which caused her pain until she died. The airplane was sold, and my father's wings were clipped, but not for long. Helicopters were his next fascination, but it would take a while for the injuries to heal before he took to the air again.

FIFTEEN

Easter Week

On the screened in porch with our bunnies circa 1974

AFTER THE ACCIDENT, we resorted to traveling the way of the rest of the world. But even in the cabin of the commercial aircraft, I still felt a twinge of discomfort, though much improved from the days when the pilot and copilot were my father and mother, so motion sickness medicine was not required anymore. On commercial flights to Louisiana, my mother was usually mistaken for the stewardess, since traveling by air required the family to dress in our new Easter outfits. This meant that I wore a pink polyester suit with a coordinating blouse. My sister wore a matching suit in cream or pale blue while my brother was forced into yellow chinos with a navy blazer and one of my father's colorful ties. My father resembled my brother, except he replaced the yellow chinos with traditional khaki pants. My mother donned her navy-blue double-breasted coat with the brass epaulets on the shoulders. Inevitably, when she walked down the aisle on her way to the cramped airline toilet, hungry passengers would flag her down and inquire about the in-flight meal. Flying was a privilege, and Easter week was an event, so we were dressed accordingly.

When we arrived at the airport in New Orleans, Aunt Marie greeted us at the gate as was done back in the days before airport security. Marie would park and venture into the terminal to weave her way through the airport so that as soon as we deplaned she was seen waving and heard unabashedly announcing our arrival to everyone in the terminal. It was as if she was announcing the arrival of a hero back from war. My father had that status in Aunt Marie's eyes. She gave him a hero's welcome each time we arrived in her home state.

My father took the driver's seat of Marie's red Buick, as Marie had traveled more than an hour from home to greet us and my father was in charge now, back at the helm of the family. As soon as his hands wrapped around the wheel of the car, my father's southern accent sneaked back into his voice. My mother rolled her eyes and braced herself for the week of my father's coronation as king and his reversal from a husband and father of three to a long-lost son returned to the bosom of his southern family. She tried to behave like the dutiful wife, but she was a spirited New Yorker, and the hailing of the king and return of the prodigal son became harder and harder to deal with. My brother, sister, and I were so glad to be in the bosom of our colorful family that we reveled in all of it.

It was a long ride, especially to a kid, but we all knew that at the end of the long, hot ride across the Atchafalaya Basin Bridge, one of the longest causeways in the United States, we would be in heaven, in the "country." The sights soon became familiar as we passed the co-op where soon we'd be buying our Easter chicks and drove past the old sharecropper homes that dotted the property. As soon as we made the left turn and the tires rubbed the steel pipes of the cattle guard, Dad sounded the horn. This was a necessary custom so that the family inside had time to freshen their drinks and head to the carport in time to greet us.

While the horn sounded, Dad surveyed his boyhood home, taking inventory of what had changed and what had stayed the same from a year earlier. He'd notice if the white picket fence needed painting, if the pecan trees were producing well, if there was one less horse in the pasture, or if the carport needed work. And, of course, the local paper sent out a photographer to document our landing on Louisiana soil, and the next day our image was on the front page of the local paper, much like local heroes.

There was so much ritual involved in our visits. We all knew our roles and the roles of others well, and we fell right in. We'd all gather on the back porch. There were no television sets, computer games, or the like. This was good, old-fashioned fun and family time. There were a half dozen wicker chairs, some rockers, and a daybed situated underneath the windows that had once been the exterior of the house before being closed in. The phone that hung on the wall was bedecked with a silver-plated handle (one of the few things still in my possession), symbolic of another era when a phone handle could be decorated. The rattling fan always spun overhead.

The reception was nothing less than stately, but my father was always atop the throne here, much to my mother's dismay, as his royal treatment unnerved her. Whenever she and my father had an argument, she would blame this doting behavior for causing his selfish view of the world. My brother, sister, and I would wait patiently amid the adult talk and the recantations of old stories about "our daddy." We had heard them all, but this one week each year was a ritual that involved hearing them again, and we never tired of them.

The reunification was not complete without highballs in thick red glasses. Aunt Marie would call for a refresher, and when my brother was too light handed with the bourbon, she'd exclaim, "Daaahlin', don't pour me such a pitiful glass." Marie loved her bourbon as much as she loved a good party, but most of all she loved that my father, her favorite nephew, was back home. It was a cause to celebrate.

There was no television in the country, but entertainment was never hard to come by. It meant sitting on the porch, swinging until late in the evening, listening to the sounds of millions of cicadas chirping. There was no need to bring any other distractions into the house; everything we needed was there. It was a place to soak in the sights and sounds of a southern family. The stories were as tall as the floor-to-ceiling windows on the screened-in porch, and the food was as authentic as the southern accents and timeless expressions of my aunts, uncles, and cousins. The home was filled with memories that spanned a century, including pictures of graduations, babies, and weddings. There were fading horse show ribbons in every color, drawers full of wrapping paper from every gift received, and charcoal drawings by my sister Christina, the aspiring young artist, hanging on the walls. We were all Aunt Marie's children, and she framed our report cards and held steadfastly on to our art projects like crocheted doilies and hook rugs. The house was brimming with sensory and aesthetic delights, and the rest of the world lay far, far away for a week.

We learned a lot in the country, even a bit of Civil War history. At Marie's, though, it was as if they were still living the Civil War, and we drove past the former slave shanties that bordered our family's plantation. It was a kind of segregation I would never have known, had it not been for my yearly week at Marie's house. When we threw a leg over our horses and set out for rides around the property, we were really careful not to ride over to the other side of the tracks. That was a shantytown.

One step too far out of the rows of beans and it was as if you were in a different place. Laundry was hung out to dry, and each house was shoddier than the next. I felt strangely out of place riding a horse for pleasure, kicking up dust in the acres and acres of plowed rows of beans while the neighbors watched from different living quarters. They knew who we were. We were the city relatives of Miss Marie, and they saw us every year and probably commented to each other how much we'd grown, but I did not know them. My father told us that some of the "homes" recently got running water and that T-Fred's family lived in one of the homes bordering the bean fields. Marie paid to have water installed for T-Fred some years before so that his house was more modernized.

We called him T-Fred, which I later learned stood for "Petite Fred." So I was speaking French for as long as I knew T-Fred without realizing it, until I asked my father what the T stood for. T-Fred was the "yard man" who had worked on Cherry Street since he was a small boy. Indoor plumbing and electricity came to T-Fred's house much later, as he lived in one of the old slaves' quarters that dotted Marie's acreage. Every day T-Fred walked over to Miss Marie's, as he called her, and she served him breakfast from his own porcelain plate and tin cup on the back porch. I remember on one of our visits, I greeted T-Fred at the door, and he asked to speak to Miss Marie. I motioned for him to come in and wait while I summoned her. Being from the North, I had never really encountered segregation. T-Fred looked at the ground, as he always did, and now was looking harder and more uncomfortably at the ground than ever. He politely declined my invitation to wait for Miss Marie in the foyer. Later my father explained that T-Fred never came into the house. I only saw T-Fred in the house once to do an in-house repair. All things outside of the home at Cherry Street were his domain. It was one of those many unwritten rules of the South that we Yankees did not understand. It was one of those things that made the South such a mystery to us northerners. I always felt awkward about this but settled for it being just the way it was at Aunt Marie's house. And I knew T-Fred and Aunt Marie looked after each other.

In the heat of the day, T-Fred would often mop the porch floors barefooted. While Marie worked, T-Fred and Willie Mays were the king and queen of the farm, and Marie would return to a cooked meal, a tidied house, and a clean yard, or "yawd," as Marie would say. T-Fred showed up for work every day save for Saturday and Sunday and worked at Cherry Street for sixty years until his death at age seventy-four. His ambition throughout his life was to someday be my father's chauffeur. He had known my father since he was a little boy and was always happy to see us on our yearly visit. My father often asked T-Fred the usual questions to show off to his kids. He'd ask about T-Fred's father, called Ole Pop, who had been a slave. T-Fred loved Aunt Marie and she loved him, but their roles were defined as only the South could do.

SIXTEEN

Cherry Street

THE ANTEBELLUM HOME of the Pavy family was built atop stilts, but the home always belonged to Aunt Marie. It was not just a home; it was a part of the family. It had a heart and soul. The old roundhouse in the backyard that housed gardening tools and rat poison had originally been the cookhouse, since plumbing and heating were not installed in the main house until much later. In the center of the house, the formal dining room had doors opening to every room. With a turn of the crystal doorknob, the inside revealed a stately table set with heavy silver utensils, starched linen napkins, and lace tablecloths for the midday meal, called dinner in these parts (it was important to know the southern transformation from lunch to dinner and dinner to supper, and I wondered why the rest of the world had it all wrong). There were etched glasses filled with wine, English teacups with delicate saucers, and a grand soup tureen filled with a Cajun delicacy.

The plantation home where Aunt Marie entertained was an extension of her, which was a perfect example of fine southern living typical of the mid-1800s. Horses roamed the outer yard of the eighty-acre estate. On every wall and atop every table there were pictures of nieces, nephews, great-nieces, and great-nephews, and numerous friends at graduations, LSU football games, and holidays, holding Easter baskets brimming with colored Easter eggs. To be part of Aunt Marie's family was an honor, and I secretly believed that I was more special than the rest of my cousins because she was appointed my godmother and never missed a chance to refer to me as her "gawdchild." They weren't rich, just southern. They were rich in soybean fields and manners, and having friends and family visit elevated their affluence.

In the middle of the yard stood a grand old oak tree, some ten feet in width, so large that it cast shadows on the old house. A large swath of ivy had stationed itself beneath the tree and encircled it. The far-reaching branches protected us from the elements while we searched for dyed Easter eggs hidden by the Easter Bunny in the monkey grass growing around the base of the tree. In the shade of the tree, Aunt Marie gave parties where guests sipped highballs—bourbon diluted with water from melting ice cubes—and remarked on its glory. There were baby showers and wedding showers, and on one vacation to Aunt Marie's house, an artist was commissioned to paint family portraits under the old oak tree.

A total of five porches surrounded the home, which was shaded by oak trees that dated to about 1850, and we sat for hours in the shade of the trees, posing statuesquely while the artist made gentle brush strokes. Those portraits were hung on a wall in Aunt Marie's bedroom to remind her of her favorite nephew's three children. And there was an oil painting done of my mother dressed in a light blue sweater, with a matching bow in her ponytail. To paint your loved ones and hang their likeness in oil was to preserve them in the manner of kings and queens, and here at Aunt Marie's house in this small Opelousas town, we were royalty simply because our grandfather, who was never mentioned, had stepped out one night and never come home. On Cherry Street it still seemed like it was yesterday. One year the century-old vines of the oak tree on Cherry Street were ripped from its trunk for fear they were killing it. And once gone, we all lamented over the loss of the tree, as its bareness was an eyesore. The vines were so dense that rabbits hid from dogs, cats hid from children, and Easter eggs were hidden there each year. We drank iced tea under its immense branches. The tree was part of the family, and we greeted it as such.

Visitors to Aunt Marie's home came and went much the same as they had done for decades, honking their horns intermittently as they traveled up the long drive past the pecan trees and the mooing cows. Even her students of the last forty years would stop in to see "Miss Marie" from time to time. Marie loved guests, and the horn-blowing custom was a sort of fanfare. Her neighbors of fifty years knew the ritual and would often call to see who had arrived.

Cherry Street, where the old house stood, was on the outskirts of town. There were ranch homes built in the thirties and forties up and down the street, but most noticeable were the ramshackle homes that lined the perimeter of the soybean fields that encircled Aunt Marie's home.

The sprawling one-story antebellum home was set back from the road. As soon as we reached the train tracks, the white picket fence came into view. The nearly eighty-acre spread was a central point in Opelousas. The rows of soybeans behind the house created an optical illusion and made the land look like it spread for miles. The oak tree obscured the view. The screened-in porch and the old porch swing awaited our arrival. The floor-to-ceiling windows allowed light into the house and access to the front porch where our favorite toy, the porch swing, hung. They opened easily on an old track with a thick chain and were painted to keep the moist air from rotting the wood. Those fabulous windows allowed cooling air movement throughout the house during the heat of the summer. It was a wonderful place to catch every little cool breeze on hot nights. In the daytime it was a place to watch the comings and goings of the company. The old train ran through daily, and Uncle Bebe reminded anyone who drove the route to cross on the bias to dampen the effect going over the old tracks, which were raised high above the pavement.

There was a trestle on the route where we rode horses. Cousin Alfred, in all of his confidence, rode atop the trestle, even though a fall from the top would land you twenty-five feet below in a muddy gorge. Even worse, if a train came there was no escape. There was a steep, but dry, route under the trestle where the horses were "given their head" so as to give them all of the benefit of being sure footed and smart enough to take the route under the trestle and back on dry ground. That train ran along the perimeter of the property, and its horn sounded loudly until it no longer needed to carry supplies from one end of the state to another and the tracks were torn up. Thrice daily the train whistle blew, and conversations were temporarily interrupted. Later the train ran twice daily, and eventually, not at all. There was no longer any need for Uncle Bebe to warn new drivers to cross the tracks "on the bias."

SEVENTEEN

Cooking Étouffée

My husband and Brother in law with Tony Chachere, famous spice icon

I NEVER SAW my mother as happy as she was when she was with Aunt Marie. Since Aunt Marie was like a mother to my father, my mother was her daughter-in-law, and they loved each other—really loved each other. The dichotomy of my sophisticated mother, who lived in the social world that her doctor husband provided, cozying up with Marie in her kitchen to make a family crawfish étouffée recipe was a sight to see. My mother was a very good cook, but southern cooking required something different—you had to be southern. So my mother took to the kitchen around noon when Willie Mays, the cook, was off for the day. I was not a baseball aficionado, so I never understood why Willie Mays's name was so fun for the adults to roll off their tongues.

Oil painting of Cherry street done in 1980

Marie had old paper milk quarts filled with frozen crawfish in étouffée sauce that had been prepared ahead of time. While they thawed in large, dented aluminum pots, the kind found in a commercial kitchen, the phone would ring from time to time. With bourbon in hand, sipping from a red highball glass, Marie would answer the phone and call Mom, who was in the kitchen diligently stirring, "Dahlin', Nell Rose and Coy are coming; add more water." A few moments later another caller would announce their impending arrival at dinner; after all, the prodigal family was visiting, and everyone wanted to pay their respects. More water was added, more rice cooked, and a midday meal was ready. When we were in the country for our yearly visits, it seemed like the old home was almost always full of people. We assumed they were all relatives, and no one was ever turned away from the grand dining table.

In the kitchen my mother continued to add water until every glass at the large formal dining table was filled, and to further accommodate all of the attendees, large bowls of starchy white rice would take up room in the large girths of my oversized southern family. Largeness in the South is a positive attribute; it is the sign of a mother who is a good cook and takes the time to enjoy fine southern cooking. I don't know if they ate all of the southern favorites all the time, but when we visited, the house was full of étouffée, bread pudding with hard sauce, dirty rice and beans, sausage jambalaya, and all of the trappings of southern hospitality. In the mornings Marie served a tray of chicory coffee so strong that they drank it from demitasse cups accompanied by sugar cubes. I was too young for coffee, but I remember my mother in her bathrobe and slippers elegantly sipping coffee around the old kitchen table with Frenchie and Marie, who peeled an orange every morning. Rituals abounded in the country like nowhere else.

The kitchen was the centerpiece of her home. And while she was not a great cook, but rather a food assembler, Aunt Marie loved food. This was where her love of red was prominent, next to her wardrobe. There were red highball glasses, red china plates, and red tins filled with her favorite snack cracker, Piggly Wiggly–brand saltines. In this old antebellum kitchen, the leaded glass cabinets went from floor to ceiling, and the only way to reach the upper cabinets was by ladder. On one of the table legs was a can opener with the Coca-Cola logo emblazoned across it. Her kitchen could have been an ad for Coca-Cola, as it was decorated entirely in red and white. In the center of Aunt Marie's kitchen was a Formica table coated with years of too-white paint. At this table a pile of young cousins congregated in the evening after a day of riding our steeds through the bean fields and dashing across creek beds. We would shed our dirty clothes and wash up in the white-enamel sink basin off the kitchen. Then we sat around that table drinking milk and eating peanut butter and jelly on soft, squishy Wonder bread from the colorful plastic bag.

It was into this kitchen that we would hurry to tell our tales of the day. First we washed our hands in the white sink basin on the back porch where T-Fred ate all of his meals. The cupboards were made of beadboard, and the porch was screened in to keep out the mosquitos. T-Fred had children who were similar in age to Ida's five boys, and all of his children went on to finish college. One even became a Rhodes scholar even though their father had only an elementary school education and worked at Aunt Marie's house all of his life.

Willie Mays was another permanent part of Cherry Street. While Aunt Marie loved to eat, she rarely cooked for herself, so that task was left to Willie Mays, one of the merriest of people to work at Aunt Marie's house. She came every day during Easter week to cook for the midday feast so that we had a large dose of Cajun cooking, and she treated us like family. She'd arrive midmorning and fill the largest stainless pot, dented from years of use. The house would fill with the smell of creole cooking and smells that were distinctly southern. During Easter week there would be so many guests, some invited and some drop-ins, and Willie Mays knew that this was the time of year when only traditional creole cooking would do to reinforce our Acadian heritage. There was andouille sausage and dirty rice one day with a dessert of bread pudding and hard sauce. Next was chicken gumbo served over a bed of dense white rice, and for dessert there would be birthday cake, and all of the April birthdays were celebrated. My sister always blew out her birthday candles at Aunt Marie's table, and every passing year is documented in the photo albums on the parlor shelf. Finally Willie Mays would serve up a crawfish étouffée in a creamy sauce that was the favorite of many. Several cardboard milk cartons of frozen étouffée usually accompanied us home to remind us of this fascinating noonday meal, but it was the people and the stories that brought it to life. Cousin Alfred would monopolize the room with his stories of fraternity adventures back in New Orleans, where he was a college student. It seemed like he was a fraternity brother most of his life, but we listened to his stories every year while his brothers Ben and James would roll their eyes at his willingness to tell his stories of impropriety. Chris did not listen at all, and Henry was usually absent. Alfred was blessed with "the gift of gab," as Aunt Marie would say, and his stories made her blush and claim, "Oh, go on now, Alfred." Telling stories in the dining room during the midday meal was my favorite part of life in the country, next to the horses.

Another yearly event in the country was the shearing of the herd of sheep that grazed in the back pasture. I never liked the shearing of the sheep. I am still not quite sure if this was a necessary thing to do, or if this yearly custom was requested by my father to teach his city kids what needed to be taught. I am sure they waited until we came to get this job done. There was more animal husbandry happening the week we were at the farm than we would see an entire year on Long Island. The sheep were gathered up by T-Fred and the older cousins, and the "sheep man," as Marie called him, came from his beat-up truck carrying electric shears. There were usually about fifteen sheep to shear, and they were hog-tied and put on the tailgate of the truck, where the sheep man took to shearing as quickly as possible, as the sheep seemed beside themselves with stress. After a few minutes with the electric shears, the sheep would come away naked and sometimes bleeding from the inevitable nicks by the large motorized scissors. They were left bleating and bleeding, which was why I never much liked this part of farm life. My father, however, acted like he possessed every skill there was on the farm, though this was the only time of year we saw him without a tie and heard a distinct southern drawl in him that caused much eye-rolling from my mother.

EIGHTEEN

Sleeping in the Country

Family gathering in the backyard

MY MOTHER AND father slept in the front room, in Papa's bed. The bed was notoriously uncomfortable, but Mom and Dad slept in it willingly, knowing the honor bestowed upon them as they slept in our great-grandfather's bed. It was the same bed that Marie had been born in, built of mahogany. The Mallard-type bed dated from about 1850 and was complete with lock and keys. It was incomplete, though, without its half tester, which was removed during one of Judge Pavy's political campaigns. There were lace curtains on every window, a large armoire in place of a closet, and a grand mantelpiece with a leaded-glass mirror. In the corner, frozen in time, was the rocking horse my father rode as a child. I am pictured riding that horse as a seven-year-old. His ears were tattered and torn, and his body needed a good bit of TLC, but he was always there; everything my father loved was still where he left it as a boy, even though he had been gone for two decades.

In Papa's room there were pictures of the esteemed judge and his children: Veazie, the oldest; the twins, Taboy and Frenchie; Sister, the reclusive one; Marie, the devoted daughter; and Ida, the youngest, who was the only one after Yvonne to bear children. She celebrated and photographed their every move, and she was like a second mother to them. These five boys filled the void left by the disappearance of her older sister and her infant son to a city far off and a state that was not Louisiana when death threats and a yearning to start over resulted in her leaving.

In the parlor, amid the red-velvet chairs, a mantel clock sat atop the walnut plantation fireplace. There were shelves filled with navy-and-gold-rimmed photo albums where I'd tuck myself away at the first chance on the King Louis loveseat within the first hour of arriving in the country. I'd nestle into the old Victorian couch and flip through every page, waiting for the ones of our Easter visit. I wanted to be apprised of everything that happened in the year since we were gone. Cousins Ben, Alfred, James, Chris, and Henry were used to Marie's antics and to their southern family; I was in awe of it all.

My sister and I shared one of two queen beds in Marie's room. The matelassé coverlet was pulled back in anticipation of our arrival. Marie slept across the room in her own queen bed, and my sister and I had difficulty sleeping under the typical noises of the fan whirling overhead and Marie's pronounced snoring. Marie would turn in by eight, then I would inspect her personal effects with a sense of fascination. Her dressers reflected another era, with bobby pins, powder puffs, and curlers. Next to her desk, a built-in closet was a treasure trove of trinkets in their original boxes. There was a silver-jade bracelet with matching clip-on earrings from a trip to Mexico. There were apples in all shapes and sizes from adoring students—some pins, others earrings—monogrammed handkerchiefs, dainty white gloves, and scarves of every color. They were the accessories of a lady.

Marie was not a rich woman, and my mother—who wore sparse jewelry of the finest quality—would smile at Marie's collection of colorful costume jewelry. Each piece told a story of a trip, of favorite students, or of a family heirloom handed down. The room fascinated me. I would open every closet to look at her assortment of pumps in every color. She usually had a new coordinating outfit purchased by my mother, who was known for her New York taste, style, and ability to shop effortlessly for clothes that others would love. On the white mantelpiece above the gas heater, there were photos mostly of us. This was Marie's room, and while her home was full of pictures, it seemed as though those who held a prominent space in her heart were pictured here.

Pictures of my grandmother, Yvonne, and my father as a baby hung in front of the fading yellow wallpaper. More heartache and more reason to dote on Carlshun, the young boy, now an esteemed New York doctor, whom they lost so many years ago to another continent and now to success and "city life."

Marie's bedroom was in the center of the house and afforded very little privacy. But Marie was not a private person. Her home, like her room, which had doors opening to Uncle Bebe's room, Papa's room, and the hallway where the Victrola rested, was open to all. We played records and danced in the parlor, which was something we never did in the suburbs of Long Island.

My brother slept in Sister's room. I don't remember where he slept when she was alive, but since she passed away in the early 1970s, her room was free for the taking. Sister's room was off the living room and boasted a queen-sized four-poster bed. The attached bathroom had the only shower in the house, and we all vied for it in the evenings. We were accustomed to showering in our own bathrooms, but in Marie's old house we took turns. Marie took only baths, and on cold nights she'd light the bathroom heater to take the chill off. During our Easter visit we had the opposite challenge of working to keep ourselves cool.

Sister's room was comfortable and private, much like Sister. There were screened-in porches on two sides. A floor-to-ceiling window opened up to the front porch, where the massive swing swayed. The other, smaller porch was where we barricaded our Easter bunnies after closing off the miniature dog door from the dachshund, Liza Jane.

NINETEEN

Rabbit Stew

My sister with her Easter bunny Circa 1970

EASTER WEEK MEANT bunnies of our own that we bought from the rabbit man. The rabbit man lived in a dilapidated house down the street from Aunt Marie, and we were all required to pick out our own rabbit even though we dreaded a visit to the old man's house. The rabbit man was a quadriplegic in a wheelchair who raised rabbits for sale, and we were dedicated customers every Easter. The house smelled of urine and rabbit pellets, and Aunt Marie paid him handsomely for the baby bunnies as a show of charity. We couldn't wait to get our rabbits and go home to begin naming and caring for them. Each day we cuddled the bunnies on our shoulders, fed them carrots and water, and loved our very own live bunny for the week. The biggest challenge was keeping them from being dog food for the dachshunds. It was their nature to kill rodents, and the bunnies were prime targets. On more than a few occasions, "accidental" slaughters required a replacement bunny.

The screened-in porch off Sister's room was chosen as home to our Easter bunnies. We would cordon off the dog doors so that Liza Jane, the dachshund, did not have access to our precious pets. We knew that keeping bunnies and animals bred as rodent killers away from each other would prove to be the most difficult task. The bunnies were usually named after cleaning supplies like Whiz, Dynamo, or Comet, and we would spend the rest of the week trying to keep them from escaping off of the back porch to become dog food. There had been so many close calls when the dachshunds, trained to get rid of rodents and pests, would regress from Aunt Marie's prized pets into bunny-chasing maniacs, as if it were their duty to rid the house of the rabbits. Inevitably the rabbits would escape from the enclosure, and hours were spent searching under the old house built on elevated piers that made a perfect spot for scared bunnies. Once all of the rabbits were accounted for, we would hand feed them rabbit pellets, carrots, and any leftovers deemed worthy. Once a day we would bring the rabbits out to one of the dog pens to let them romp in the Kentucky bluegrass.

One year I chose a rabbit with a defect. Its head was permanently cocked to the left, which made eating and drinking virtually impossible. When the defect was noticed, Aunt Marie pledged to fix the situation by bringing the damaged little white bunny back to the rabbit man and replacing it with a new one.

I would have none of it. First because I could not stomach another trip to the rabbit man's house, and second because I had already become attached to the frail white rabbit. I was not going to exchange the rabbit I dubbed Tide, and I vowed to hand feed her and use a dropper to get vital fluids into her. She had great difficulty romping in the grass and nearly became dog food more than once, as she could not run quickly, so keeping her alive for the long week was especially tricky. When our week in the country was over, however, I became adamant that the bunny must come home with me. I feared she would become rabbit stew and would die of starvation without my care. After much pleading, my mother finally agreed to let the rabbit come home on the airplane with us. My insistence got the best of her, and while my brother and sister kissed their rabbits goodbye one last time, I gathered up my little fur ball for the long ride to the airport. Once at the terminal, we said our goodbyes to Aunt Marie, who left strong red lipstick outlines on the faces of us all. We then entered the screening area, but security spotted the fluffy animal and told us the rabbit would not be allowed on the plane. In disbelief and horror and with tear-soaked cheeks, I handed my misshapen friend to Aunt Marie, who was forced to take custody. I'll never forget the vision in red waving goodbye with one hand and cradling Tide in the other. As was our custom, we never asked what happened to the rabbits after Easter; we knew they became rabbit stew.

Years later, when Cousin Daniel was five or six and visiting Cherry Street for our annual crawfish boil, the younger generations ambled over to the rabbit pens to admire our prized pets while the rest of the adults sipped highballs and watched Ben season the boiling crawfish. Daniel was excitedly trying to catch one of the larger bunnies to play with. Scared rabbits are fast creatures, but before we knew it, Daniel had caught the bunny and held it proudly in his arms, stroking its soft fur. The bunny, not used to this youthful attention, writhed, flung itself out of his grasp, and landed with a thump onto its head. The rabbit lay at Daniel's feet as still as a sack of flour, and the boy wondered why it had suddenly ceased playing. The older cousins scurried the little ones out of the pen and excused the rabbit's sudden lack of playful energy, not wanting to leave an emotional scar for Daniel having killed the loveable animal. I still wonder if Daniel knows what really happened in that rabbit pen. We spent the rest of the crawfish boil trying to avoid letting the cat out of the bag while Daniel's father, Alfred, dug a small hole to bury the bunny. That was the last year the Easter bunnies came to live on Cherry Street, as we were all getting too old for bunny rabbits anyway, and the adults decided that the emotional toll of caring for the rabbits, watching them maimed, and leaving them behind was too problematic. So adopting Easter bunnies was a tradition that Aunt Marie finally ended, but she continued to visit the rabbit man every Easter to make a donation.

TWENTY

Dachshunds and Other Animals

My brother with Cousins Chris and Ben getting ready to shear the sheep

WE ALL HEARD the stories about the animals that my father be-friended during the long, hot days when he was a visitor to the South. He and his cousin, Octave, spent the summer being supervised by Aunt Marie, who was on summer break from her job as a schoolteacher of "Looooosiana" history, and who delighted in caring for her favorite sister's young son. The pain they felt for this child who had lost his father in a tragic event was keen, and they showered him with all the love they could muster. They spent the summer making up for the loss of a young father and tried to heal the scars that history had left on the family. Animals of all kinds were commissioned to make life in the country idyllic. The dachshunds served dual purposes as pets and pest control.

In the thirty-plus years I visited the South, there were always little red-coated dachshunds at Aunt Marie's house, and all carried the name Liza Jane, followed by one, two, three, four, and so on. They were always full-sized red females, and it was difficult to know if it was the same one from year to year unless one added the proper numeral at the end. They were never allowed in the house but lived on the back porch and had their own little yard with a dog door for self-walking, which led onto the screened-in porch and back out to the yard. Dogs were not inside animals in the country but were only rodent deterrents there—unless my father was visiting.

My father delighted in reacquainting himself with them each year, and it was as if each one was the original Liza Jane he grew up with as a young boy. He would scoop the excited wiener dog up, supporting its long, wriggling back, and kiss its snout with a vigor I had rarely seen my father do with any animal. After the initial meeting and number learning, there was rarely any contact with Liza Jane until the goodbye a week later, where my father would exercise the same enthusiasm and snout kissing and vow to see her again next year.

The family dog back in the suburbs of Long Island was a sweet black poodle named Morgan who was practically invisible to us all, but here in "the country," the animals were a part of life. My father had grown up with pigs and goats that were his friends. Because he was the only child for many years until the first of his cousins, Henry, was born, the animals were his playmates. His favorites were Billy, Nana, Brownie, and Trixie Marshall Minx, the goats. One year the ten-year-old Carlshun and Bruce Hidalgo, the neighbor boy, trained Billy, the goat, to pull a small red wagon around the farm and then ambitiously tried to train a small colt to do the same. Unfortunately the colt got frisky when that wagon was tied to its haunches with rope and knots, and it reared high enough to kick Bruce, who was leading the horse while Little Carl sat in the wagon, square in the front teeth, knocking them out.

He had a passel of pigs that he loved. A particular favorite was Blanchette, aptly named for her smooth white skin. It was only summers that he saw his farm animals, but he fed and cared for his furry and feathered friends each year and told stories about them to his children for years to come. This city boy had an attachment to his mother's childhood home and it to him. It was an escape to a lost place; it was a place that time held on to, and he was the heir to it all. His animal husbandry skills were honed.

Cows roamed the property from year to year. As a youngster, Father would milk the cows every morning in the summer when he was visiting from the big city. He and T-Fred milked five or six every morning and fastened them to a fence with leg irons on their hind legs to prevent the inevitable kicking. Once a bucket was filled with milk, T-Fred took it to the back porch, where the separator, a device with an array of different-sized funnels, sat. The separator created a cream that was eventually churned into butter. The leftovers, or whatever could not be used, became "clabber" for the chickens. This country life for an orphaned city boy was like heaven, and he would regularly become ill eating the rich cream and fresh figs gathered from the backyard.

The henhouse was a crapshoot every year. There were some years that we city kids—my brother, sister, and I—headed out to the henhouse each morning to fill a basket with farm-fresh eggs. Some years the henhouse was the scene of carnage when animals had made their way in and decimated the flock. A trip to the co-op was a visit to another world for us city kids. The old wooden warehouse from the co-op, filled with all kinds of feed, was teaming with screaming baby chicks. It was as if everyone in the county raised chickens every year. It was clear that Aunt Marie just wanted us to experience the thrill of caring for baby chicks and collecting our own eggs. The henhouse was a short walk from the house, near the hay barn. I was not the country girl my sister was, and even the chickens scared me. My brother was indifferent. Eggs to eat? Great. My sister loved everything about the country back then and was as confident in the henhouse as she was in the horse barn. There were years when the eggs were plentiful and had to be collected and shared with the neighbors, and there were years when there were none.

As we got older and Aunt Marie got older, the henhouse fell into disrepair, and there were no more fresh eggs, as she could not care for all of the animals. When we were all younger, the cousins would stop over weekly to care and collect, but when they went off to college, some things had to go. Aunt Marie was, after all, the caretaker of all people and things, and she was aging. It was my father who really loved the fresh eggs from the country.

A day or two before Easter Sunday, Willie Mays was seen tending a large, steaming pot of water filled with eggs. It was her job to hard-boil eight or more dozen eggs in preparation for dyeing. This was a tradition that was done every year and was a highlight. On the scheduled day, usually arranged by my mother and Aunt Marie, the youngest cousins were instructed to meet on the back porch, where there were boxes of PAAS-brand egg-dyeing kits atop old newspapers. The back porch was typically T-Fred's domain, but on egg-dyeing day, the young cousins took over his lunch spot. There were wire egg holders and stickers of baby chicks in Easter designs. At one of four stations for my siblings and Cousin Chris, there were small containers of dye in a variety of pastel colors. For the better part of the afternoon, we dipped and applied decorations to eggs, covering the counters with egg dye, none of which was a problem for this outside room equipped with white steel cabinets from the 1920s that were considered vermin proof and were hardly fazed by the egg-dyeing mess. Aunt Marie filled the battered, old stainless steel pot with so many eggs that I would bet that she cleaned out the egg aisle from the Piggly Wiggly that morning. Nothing was too much for us, and no amount of indulgence was off limits. Eggs in pale shades of pink, yellow, blue, green, and purple were laid on an old cotton towel to "set" and were finally piled high in a large basket where they were later given to the Easter Bunny. We waited for the bunny to hide the eggs in the vines of the oak tree. The hunt was the most awaited event of the year for the children, but for my Aunt Marie, Easter Sunday Mass was one of the holiest days for this devout Catholic.

Not only is Easter the highest holiday, but for Aunt Marie,

it was especially so because she was accompanied to her church by her favorite nephew and his family. We usually arrived early to save the first and second pew for close family. The outfit for Easter Sunday Mass at the "big church," as we called it, was carefully selected by my mother to show us off, as she knew the entire congregation took notice of us. It was as if everyone took notice of the outsiders from the city, or the family of the slain son. It could have been that our garb was important because we were a spectacle due to our past, or my mother felt it was her job to show off her own New York fashion sense. She liked to make it clear that she was not from this part of the world and had no desire to acquiesce to the norms in the country; she was a city girl. Sitting through the highest and longest Mass of the year was a chore. After the service we made the traditional yearly pilgrimage to the nearby graveyard to pay our respects to family members who had passed on.

A game of "Petit Bout and Gros Bout" played out for the rest of the afternoon until all eggs were suitably smashed and ready to make into egg salad. The basic idea is to determine whose boiled chicken egg is the hardest as two people tap their eggs together until it cracks and is considered "dead." But if only one side cracks, then it is still in the game and free to crack against other eggs. We played until all of the eggs were dead and used the dead eggs to make batches of egg salad. I never questioned this game or saw it again. It was just another one of the anomalies that came with life in Opelousas, and I loved it. Egg salad is still one of my favorite dishes.

Twenty-One

Horse Love

Uncle Bebe with Christina and I with Cousins Alfred and Ben

My father was not an animal person at home, but in the country, these animals took on different meanings. Almost as soon as he arrived in the country, he would stroll out to the horse barn to see which nags were alive from year to year. On the first morning of our arrival in the country, we'd all wake early, dress in old jeans and T-shirts, and converge upon the horse barn to find our favorite steeds awaiting our arrival. The horses spent most of their time free in the pasture eating grass, and so when we arrived to put them to work for our pleasure, they were none too thrilled to see us. The horses worked harder during Easter week than all of the rest of the weeks combined. Sugar cubes were abundant, and Tonto was always in need of a good brushing.

In the tack room, where the sweet feed was stored in fifty-gallon ceramic bins to keep away the mice, the saddles and bridles accumulated a year of dust. We had been taught all the proper horse etiquette from cousins Ben and Alfred when they were in their teens and drove across town to care for Aunt Marie's horses after Uncle Bebe died. They fancied themselves cowboys and taught their young city cousins how to ride Western. When Bebe was alive, the horses and cows had a purpose as his farm friends, but when he was gone, the only time they got attention was when my cousins, by then teenagers, wanted to show off their horsemanship or impress a friend with their command of horse beasts.

We did well for city kids, and we loved the horses. I had a love-hate relationship, as I was scared of their bigness. My sister was the horsewoman, and she learned to command them and bend them to her will. The cousins schooled us in how to put on a bridle and harness a horse. We learned that you never put a harness blanket on without properly currycombing in a circular direction and cleaning the hooves using a hoof pick to dislodge dirt and debris, which there was a lot of as the horses in the country spent most of their time out to pasture. We knew not to mess with the "frog" on a horse's foot, as it is sensitive and acts as the shock absorber when a horse moves. Everything we used had a year's worth of dust and dirt on it. Saddles and bridles were affixed to the horses, and we'd be off on a ride through the dusty soybean fields that covered the eighty acres of the family farm. They were neatly plowed and created an illusion that made the land look like it spread for miles. Our travels to the "back pasture," as my father called it, were an adventure; no one had been to these parts since we left last Easter, and we were warned to be careful of strangers trespassing on the property.

The old trestle was our first destination. We'd ride our horses carefully across, hoping they wouldn't falter on the long, high stretch. The thought of the train making an unannounced trip made our hearts beat loudly until we had each arrived safely on the other side. We rode across dry irrigation ditches, through rickety barbed wire gates, and full speed through the bean fields at a gallop, exploring all the familiar places. Sometimes we would forgo the trip to the back pasture and set up a game of capture the flag in the front pasture, where the adults watched from under the shade of the oak tree. We rode until we saw the cars of aunts and uncles, cousins and friends, sounding the horns to announce their arrival. It meant it was time to dismount and head to the dinner table for the midday meal.

We each had a favorite horse, except my brother, who rode whichever horse he was asked to ride; he rode by default. We were in the country, there were farm animals, and he was expected to participate. He was a good sport about riding horses. I was scared to death, my sister was in love with horses, and Carl just did as he was told, so he rode Tonto, a large paint horse with lightly colored eyes that looked at us as if he could see right through us. He had large brown-and-black spots that covered his mostly white fur, and his brown mane was long and unkempt. If Tonto was too hard for us to catch, Bebe would fill a cup with sugar cubes and round him up easily. Since Tonto was the biggest horse, we always rode him double, as there were only four horses in the country and usually five cousins. Tonto looked wild with his white coat and black spots. I was scared of him when I was on the ground, but if I was on his back, I just made sure not to fall, as he was about sixteen-hands high. He had one light-blue eye and looked like the horse in the story of Miss Jane Pittman, that killed one of the slaves when he tried to ride him. The slave went out one day, and the next day the horse returned with the dead man dragging behind with one foot still attached to the stirrup. I could never forget that scene after watching the TV movie as a young girl. Tonto looked like he could throw a rider and leave them for dead.

These were farm animals, and the only time they got steady attention was during our visit. I could not handle Tonto, and a gentle and well-mannered horse had to be carefully picked for me, the easily breakable youngest child. My sister was the horse-woman and the only Louisiana-born child of the family. For some reason, that fact changed things. She was a real country girl because of this and required a more serious steed, one that she could show off her riding prowess on. I loved to feed sugar cubes to Tonto, but I was generally scared of horses and he was tall, so it was a long fall from his haunches. Cousin Al tried to give us all lessons in how to fall off a horse and gave us each an opportunity to practice. He explained the tuck-and-roll technique and encouraged us to practice. I avoided this activity and was given freer rein because my fear was evident. I was not game for the horse life like my sister, and I was able to hide behind my mother, who easily exempted her baby girl from such dangerous pastimes. I continued to ride the docile animals.

Dot, the old Bombay pony we rode forever, was a trusted

horse and my favorite,. She was short-legged, and a fall to the ground from her was not nearly as painful as from the others. The younger ones rode her because she was gentle and slow, kept us close to the ground, and stood only about eleven hands. I loved to ride them, but horses scared me. I'd walk up to them, one hand outstretched and ready to run to the fence if they acted "spooked" or showed any sign of moving their hindquarters toward me. I could climb the fence quickly if needed. My brother went along with the gag, but he was not a "horse person" either and rode them purely for entertainment. He never developed a bond with any of them, but Dot was my personal favorite. I always rode her through the bean fields, and I felt safe because the ground was so close. I could practically reach down and touch it. A fall from Dot was a minor event.

Traveler looked like a real horse and was harder to ride. Ben and Alfred took special care of Traveler for my sister, since she could only see her once a year. Christina was the real horse girl, and she knew how to put on the bridle, how to cinch the girth tightly under a horse's belly, and how to use a currycomb. Bebe taught us all that we had to groom the horses each time before we rode them. We all knew that the horses had a tendency to suck in their bellies when the girth was being tightened. These were not serious horses; they were country nags we loved to ride once a year, but they knew that our arrival meant hot and sweaty runs through the soybean fields. They were unconditioned animals that knew the city kids would kick and cajole them into sprints across Marie's fields just for fun, but they also knew that sugar cubes would follow every ride. We would fill our hands with as many cubes as possible and giggle as the horses nosed them around in our hands and then pulled them into their big-gummed mouths.

Nelly was a feisty pony who belonged to the youngest cousin, Chris, who lived across town and was considered the horse person, next to my sister. She was even hard to brush, as she would toss her head from side to side and knock us over occasionally. Then there was the year we were playing capture the flag. The front pasture was free enough of trees and flat enough to serve as our field for the yearly event. Goals were established and teams were set. My sister was in charge, and she rode the most spirited horse, Traveler, named after Robert E. Lee's horse, which he resembled. He was a dapple gray. I rode Dot, who was old and slow and had a matted mane but suited me. My brother rode Tonto, who was big and awkward but had been around for the longest and did whatever he was asked, much like my brother.

Cousin Chris's pony, Nelly, was spunky and smart, and Chris knew how to handle her. The game was two on two, and the flag went round and round. Easily bored and starving, we all turned our horses and headed home as soon as we heard the call for lunch, galloping, excited, and carefree. Tonto loped ahead, Traveler was fast, Dot trotted as fast as her little legs would go, and Chris tore ahead on his new pony, crossing the elevated blacktop driveway. The driveway was a long, narrow swath through a meandering field, treeless but for the nine pecan trees planted by my father one year, which never produced.

Once upon the blacktop, Nelly made a sharp turn, and Chris was thrown over her head with an impossible landing on the hardest surface around without so much as a hand to block. I trotted closer, heard him moan, and saw the pool of blood, and instinct told me to run far away. I turned Dot's head, kicked, and ran. My brother, the one who eventually became a doctor, and who was all of thirteen at the time, sat with Chris, soothed him, and talked to him while my sister ran for help. The adults were nearby in the house, but the walk to the front pasture, with Chris bleeding and losing consciousness on Marie's driveway, took an eternity, or so I later learned. I hid in the barn, tucked into the straw, until I felt safe enough to come out. The ambulance had come and gone to take Chris to the nearby hospital, where he had lost several teeth, had a broken jaw wired shut, and suffered a severely battered and bruised face. The impossibility of the fall and all of the soft landings that he could have made left us telling and retelling the story for many years. Not only were the scars and reconstructive surgeries remembered but Nelly was not the chosen pony after that Easter vacation, and she was looked at with an air of unpredictability. Only those experienced riders were allowed on top of the rambunctious pony after the capture the flag game that ended in such bloodshed.

TWENTY-TWO

The Gold and the Purple

Ida and Marie headed to an LSU game

WHILE RED WAS the color that Aunt Marie clothed herself in, she cheered for the gold and purple—"Poiple," as she called it. I loved to watch her speak and would watch the saliva pool in the cracks of her gentle, well-worn mouth. She was so powdered, so ladylike, that it was hard to believe that she was a diehard football fan. I remember watching her dress for the bus ride to Baton Rouge to watch her boys play football. And many of them over the years really were her boys. She'd been their teacher at Opelousas High School, and when they went on to don the gold-and-purple LSU football jerseys, Marie cheered for them as if she had birthed them, not just taught them. After she'd applied the last layer of powder, she would tuck tissues in her handbag, to be used to dab the corners of her mouth.

It was a long bus ride but not one that she'd consider missing. The bus was chartered by other LSU fans who made the long journey on I-10 together when driving late at night became a chore for the older fans, yet staying home to listen to the game was a last resort. One of the boys would join Marie for the pilgrimage to LSU stadium where Tiger Country was proclaimed loudly. Southerners are proud of their football teams. Usually James or Ben, the dutiful ones, would accompany their old aunt. "Old Aunt" was the term Marie used to describe herself, and she'd smile demurely. She loved her nephews and would do anything for them.

Cousin Coy was her football companion. Nobody knows if she really was our cousin. She was somebody's cousin and a relation of Marie's—they were double cousins. Everybody was related to Marie. Whenever we went somewhere with Marie, the introduction would be followed by a lengthy explanation of how they were somehow related to Marie and, hence, related to me. It was all very confusing, but it was safe to say that we were related to the whole town, and everyone called her "Aunt Marie," like they wanted her for their very own. So Cousin Coy, a nurse, who smoked a pack of unfiltered Pall Mall cigarettes a day and was grossly overweight, and Marie, adorned in red, carrying a purse with nothing but rosary beads and Wrigley's chewing gum, were an unlikely pair but were best of friends and kinfolk. Their camaraderie included highballs, bridge, yearly trips to New York (you guessed it, "New Yoik" to Marie), and LSU games where they were regulars.

Cousin Coy dressed in clothes from Lane Bryant, which carried plus sizes, bought by my mother, the personal shopper for the oversized or underconcerned-about-fashion-sense family that she married into. But Coy was so lovable and called everybody "dahlin'" with an unfiltered cigarette between her lips; even my neatly groomed and well-appointed mother would traipse through the aisles of our hometown Lane Bryant and buy the finest plus-size outfits for the plus-sized woman and box them for shipment south. A skirt or pair of slacks was always matched with a coordinating shirt. My mother taught me early on that it was always important to buy a matching top, or the bottoms would wind up stuffed into a closet and never worn if there was not a top readily available to pair it with. Coy suffered from severe emphysema but would rather have died than give up her pack-a-day habit (come to think of it, she did die rather than give up her cancer sticks).

Marie never smoked a day in her life, apparently because Wrigley's spearmint gum was her oral vice. After a long bus ride accompanied by other diehard fans plied with highballs, the pair would cheer loudly for every touchdown accomplished by their boys. They were Louisianans, and even if Coy never had the opportunity to teach them, they were her boys too. When Marie was older, after several knee surgeries (caused, my father said, by her weight gain over the years), she was less apt to stand and cheer for every touchdown. The failing knees kept her in her seat, and she'd resort to tugging on the sleeve of the loyal nephew who joined her on the journey, usually Ben or James, and ask who scored the TD and if he was black or white. She was glad all the same if it was one of her boys, but color was still a factor in Marie's world.

Years after her death, the team of gold and purple, many of whom had never heard of Aunt Marie, much less been taught by her, made it to top honors by winning the BCS National Championship. When LSU won the Sugar Bowl, it evoked a bit of nostalgia for many familiar with our aunt Marie, who had not lived to see the victory. The state went wild; they had finally done it, and I thought about my aunt Marie.

I was not alone; a writer for the *Sports Illustrated* special edition devoted entirely to the LSU football team winning the Sugar Bowl was also thinking about her. Maybe he was related too. It seemed odd that a complete stranger referred to my aunt Marie as "one of the greatest LSU fans of all time." This author penned a column in *Sports Illustrated* devoted to the subject of my aunt Marie. My father called to tell me the news that *Sports Illustrated* had recognized my aunt Marie as a diehard LSU football fan. I thought that was just how we knew her.

There it was for the world to see that my (our) aunt Marie was being recognized, and then I learned that the author was, in fact, not related, and I could go back to calling her my aunt Marie. I learned that the author had been a student in one of her "Looooosiana" history classes. He told the story of his teacher giving him the greatest compliment a high school boy growing up in the Deep South, surrounded by "Tiger Country" signs, can get. Aunt Marie told him that if he practiced really hard, maybe one day he would wear the gold-and-purple jersey and play in Tiger Stadium.

As we got older, another one of our favorites, "drive-through hurricanes"—not the weather-related kind, but the tall, frothy passion fruit-colored drinks served in disposable plastic cups—were introduced. Drinking alcohol was a part of my Cajun family, and the nuances of Louisiana's open container laws were remarkable to me even as a teenager. It seemed as though it was perfectly acceptable to consume alcohol in public as long as it was done in a paper cup and seemingly even if underage, as I was. I remember my first drive-through with my cousin Chris.

Being Easter week, as we called it, Chris was out of school for our annual visit. It would have been a shame to send him to school while his cousins were visiting. He took the week off of whatever he was doing to spend all of his time playing with his Yankee cousins. He had just gotten his driver's license, and we were both underage. No matter—we were in Louisiana, and he was a local boy. Proof of age was optional. On one trip, Cousin Chris and I were leaving Cherry Street to go across town to the Opelousas Tennis and Swim Club when he pulled up next to the seedy-looking shack with a sign proclaiming "Hurricanes Here" in bold letters. From inside our Aunt Marie's red Buick, the car she lent us on our Easter trips, we placed an order for two hurricanes and drove back out into traffic to continue our journey, just two underage drinkers using the convenience of drive-through liquor. "Only in Louisiana," I'd say to myself.

When I visited Louisiana eight years after the passing of my great-aunt Marie, it was to attend a family wedding. It was the first wedding of the nieces and nephews (my second cousins once removed), but it was the first time the Yankees had been back in a while. "You need a passport to come to Looosiana," my cousin Al quipped. And he was right. I remember my own wedding twenty years earlier when a large faction of Cajun

Gretchen Dubit

cousins made the trip to New York to the nuptials planned by my mother.

Al, then in his mid-thirties, sported a Tom Selleck mustache and the same grin that rendered his eyes invisible when he began to charm a crowd. He had pirated the microphone from the band and was beginning to speak. My mother always loved Al, and he had been indulged as a young boy, as he had a penchant for stories. His was a gift, and each story grew more raucous as he grew older and became a frat boy. Al never grew up and was proud of his indiscretions, though he became less and less a favorite as he resorted to telling the same frat-boy stories well into his forties. Whenever Al came to the country on respites from his studies at LSU, he told stories of being a DKE. It was a fraternity that reveled in being bad boys who cleaned up well, and when I was a young girl, he implored me to come to LSU and take studies in how to be a "sexy-tary." My mother was none too pleased, and Alfred's stature as the favorite fell hard and fast.

Some years later, at my New York wedding, Al stood cradling the microphone in his hand until he was sure he had a captive audience, as only he could. My mother came close to pulling the cord but instead resorted to some eye-rolling in anticipation of his "speech."

He began, "Back in Louisiana, we have this custom," and now I was engaged in some eye-rolling of my own but wanted to hear where he would go with this story. "The custom," he went on, "is that the older brother of the groom, if unmarried,"—and not coincidentally, Gregg's older brother, Scott, was still single—"has to dance in a bucket of ice water." Two waiters hired for the soiree carried in a large bucket brimming with water, and Scott rolled up his pant legs. The band played and he danced, splashing water all over the parquet floor erected in the backyard for the event. So as the band played, we clapped and laughed until Big Al, as we called him, once again sidled up to the microphone. My mother surely pondered whether to grab the microphone and send him to his seat. But Al was a grown man, and she let him continue reluctantly.

This time he said, "Another part of this southern custom is the older sister of the groom, who is unmarried"—Gregg's sister perked up—"has to dance with the mop." And a mop was presented to his older, unmarried sister to mop the soaked dance floor.

This "custom" had never been heard of before, and I am sure has never been seen again, but the local paper, upon covering the event, was able to chronicle the antics of Big Al and the southern flair with which he was able to entertain the very skeptical crowd. Al, in southern style, was once again able to steal the show at the wedding of his second cousin once removed.

Twenty-Three

Crawfish Boils

My brother catching Crawfish Circa 1978

The year after I was married, it was time to visit the country and get a dose of family life in Opelousas, the city that calls itself the spice capital of the world. And who could forget that the Yambilee Festival happens each October and continues throughout the weekend with events including concerts, cooking competitions, a parade, and beauty pageants. Louisiana still prides itself on its beauty pageants and the "queening and princessing" of young girls. Aunt Marie was always up for the challenge of treating new guests in Opelousas to a place where time forgot to march on. She did not have to try very hard to give all who visited the royal treatment. It was not the fine-linens and upgraded-bathrooms type, but the kind that made all guests feel as though their presence was an honor. At the first sound of the horn, it was clear that we were someplace very different. I remember how I felt making the turn off Cherry Street. It was like turning into a magical place, and now I was about to share it with my new husband, a veritable foreigner.

Even though his older sister had gone to college in New Orleans, he would never forget his first visit to Cherry Street and the cast of characters who made up my Louisiana family. At the mere mention of a newcomer, a crawfish boil was planned—even better, a catch-your-own-crawfish boil.

The carport was the venue for our yearly crawfish boil. Cousin Ben called upon his crawfish connection as if he were making an illicit drug deal, and the cost of the little critters would be a hot topic. The crawfish crop generally wavered from year to year and began as soon as the writhing crustaceans were sprung from the blue woven sacks. We all commented on their girth, excited to suck the heads and eat the tails. Forty or fifty pounds was usually enough to subdue the crowds. There were aunts and uncles from all over town who would attend this annual event held during Easter week. Marie would drag out her card tables and set them under the lighted carport so that we could amass large piles of empty shells after the sun had gone down. She covered the tables with newspaper and set out all available chairs.

Cousin Ben was in charge of the evening, and it was necessary to commend his prowess in procuring the crawfish. The cooks heated large pots of water and added the perfect mix of spices. They set out ketchup from the Piggly Wiggly (Aunt Marie referred to it as "her" grocery store often) mixed with

Worcestershire sauce, and when the first lot was boiled to perfection, the competitive eating began. Beer and crawfish were the main staples. Marie, who was not a cook but rather a connoisseur of southern cuisine, knew that was all that was necessary to please the crowd.

The year my husband first visited the South, he spent a lot of time asking questions about all of our bizarre customs. The crawfish boil was a particular eye-opener. His gluttonous eating impressed even Uncle Octave, who usually arrived in his one-piece khaki suit with a full-front zipper for comfort while digging for the largest crustacean. Octave donned that familiar one-piece suit on a trip to see us in New York one year. Much to my mother's dismay, it was his outfit of choice for an evening in the Big Apple to see a Broadway show the last year he visited. Trendiness and fashion are not important in Opelousas, and this was difficult for my mother, for whom being a hick was not an option; she could not even fake it for a week. She stayed elegant throughout the week even while eating fried chicken salad at the Opelousas diner. She was teased about her high-mindedness, but all the cousins secretly admired her for her beauty and style. Her New York roots were obvious. She was not a southern belle and did not like to pretend to be one. Perhaps that is why my father chose her, a departure from his large southern family.

Octave in his one-piece suit was just one more thing we all looked forward to seeing at our yearly crawfish boil, where competitive eating was taken to a new level. We practically kept a scorecard of how many crawfish were downed. I'll never forget the glee in my husband's eyes when he saw that a total lack of manners was completely acceptable at the table. We all ate standing up, hovering over the table, moving from pile to pile when the mountain of crawfish shrank. Aunt Marie cleaned up the tables with one fell swoop of the newspapers, and the stench of fish hung in the carport for days.

When we were younger, a day of fishing in the bayou for our own dinner was the custom. Uncle Albert instructed his boys, Alfred, Ben, and James, the older cousins (except for Henry who was so much older than my siblings and me that he was usually far away) to take us to the bayou. Often we drove for miles across the flatness of Louisiana to a muddy swamp that was said to have a copious crop. With sun hats, sneakers, and long pants, we walked knee-deep into the swampy bayou to strategically place our nets. Made with rope and affixed to wire, the net itself was where chunks of meat were attached with a safety pin. We were each responsible for checking our own nets, and I remember how I felt, walking amid the crawling, clawed creatures in mud-like quicksand. Inevitably, the helpless, writhing creatures would become prey to a game of toss, and we'd squeal in delight and disgust as crawfish were thrown about with the aim of their tiny pinchers latching on to one of the cousins.

Cousin Ben planned the day in the swamps; he'd check the weather and consult some fishing buddies. Water temperature and hours of sunlight were the two big drivers of an early season for crawfish (or crawdads, as the locals called them), but the rule of thumb for the season was Super Bowl through the Fourth of July. This was one of our favorite annual outings, and we, the small cousins, guided by Cousin Ben, headed to the fishing grounds. Ben was the fourth in line of our five male cousins born to Ida, Marie's youngest sister. School had not been his forte, so Ben was the one who tried his hand at many things, including raising cattle on the family land. He gravitated toward jobs that required knowledge of animal husbandry or weather patterns. While his brothers went into more intellectual careers, Ben used his hands. He was the hardworking one of the family, and his brawn was what he was known for. Crawfishing was just one of his pastimes, and he used this to make some extra cash in season. We never missed a day in the mud looking for crawdads.

We crawfished rain or shine, but the best time for crawfish was springtime, when water temperatures heated up into the sixties. We'd fill a cooler, mostly with beer for the older boys, and head out in Marie's old red Buick to the family land. We were keenly aware that these fields were property of the family, and there were acres and acres of wetlands good for nothing but fishing for crawfish. Cousin Ben would proudly survey the mostly underwater paddy fields, as if they were prime real estate, until he found a spot down a rutted dirt road where we unloaded buckets and nets and stood knee-deep in the mud, setting traps filled with slabs of meat fastened with safety pins. A long stick was used to check the traps. When we were certain that the slimy creatures had affixed themselves to the netting of the traps, the bounty was hauled up and heads were counted. The haul was dumped into buckets. Crawdads pricked our fingers and were flung to and fro in crawdad wars. The mud enveloped our feet deep into the water, and we heard great sucking sounds when it was time to move and check a trap. The sun beamed overhead, and we all came home as red and burned as the shell of a crawfish. It was a long, hot day in the swamps, but when those buckets of crawfish were poured into Ben's oversized tin pots to boil for the day, standing in that thick, gooey mud was worth it.

Twenty-Four

Aunt Marie Ages

My sister and I with our husbands visiting Cherry Street Circa 1992

CHANGE WAS A rare thing on Cherry Street, but when visits to the hospital for what Aunt Marie called "a little fall" began occurring more frequently, my father and Marie's youngest sister, Ida, spoke in hushed tones about sending her to a nursing home. They were left with the responsibility of caring for Aunt Marie and the affairs of the estate. As evidence of her unwavering desire to continue to live alone on Cherry Street, Aunt Marie told untruths about her injuries. And when she fell while reaching for the ceiling fan's pull cord to slow its speed, as she had always done in those hot Opelousas summers, she minimized her injuries.

Marie was less and less agile each year; the woman who seemed so childlike and full of life was growing old. She had now become a legend to a new generation of Pavy offspring, the children of her beloved nephews, and they would have some stories to tell, but my sister's kids, my brother's kids, and my own children would never meet her. Reluctantly, Aunt Marie went to the nursing home, and "the country" slowly faded into history. When Aunt Marie's presence was gone, weeds and overgrowth from two years of neglect obscured the majestic house from view. My father worried that vandals might pillage the old house, still filled with furnishings and memories.

My country cousins had attempted to continue some of the traditions like Christmas and birthday celebrations in the front parlor, but it was painful for Marie to just "visit" her lifelong home. As Aunt Marie grew older and the rest of us grew up, every family member fantasized about living on Cherry Street and keeping the traditions alive, but the reality of refurbishing the old house so it met the standards of modern living was daunting. Each bathroom was equipped with a gas wall heater that was lit with large strike-anywhere matches, and matchboxes sat atop all the bathroom heaters. Eventually we all came to our senses and realized the impracticality of moving the old home; it belonged here beneath the swaying cypress trees, near the soybean fields and the crumbling red-roofed barns and outbuildings that dotted the landscape on Cherry Street, and the oak tree whose long branches were the only means of cooling the old house in the heat of the Louisiana summers.

Under this same tree, the sounds of Aunt Marie's voice resonated across the old plantation; from high atop our horses, we saw her red glow all the way across the pasture. She'd return from her work as a teacher of history at the local high school.

"I teach Luziana history," she'd say in her thick southern accent, specific to Acadiana, as the region is called. So thick was her accent that she had words of her own. Words like "pois," meaning the red-leather bag filled with her personal effects, including Wrigley's spearmint gum in the green wrapper.

"I don't smoke; I chew," she'd say while holding out a stick. Rarely did people refuse it; she was the kind of woman you wanted to please. She had an uncanny ability to change everyday words, phrases, and situations into sheer amusement. To engage her was to be entertained by a gentle southern woman. There was charm in the way she offered gum; one would be a fool not to oblige her.

Eventually, when Aunt Marie was gone, it was time to decide what to do with the old house. My siblings and I could not bear to go back to Opelousas to visit; Aunt Marie was not there. There was talk of turning it into a park, but Opelousas is not a wealthy town, and that idea fell through. Next came selling the property off to Walmart, as it was large enough to build a super-center in the middle of town. Luckily this idea did not come to fruition either. Then my father was approached by a couple who were historians and had an idea to buy the old house and move it to a new spot to be restored as their family home. My father sold the house for a dollar on a handshake. The house was moved piece by piece and reproduced exactly as it had been. The last detail was the whitewashed picket fence that was taken down and now encircled the same home in its new place. It had been restored to its former self. My father reported that his mother's childhood home had gotten a facelift and was lovingly restored to its former glory. The new owners were painstaking in their details and preservation of the house and its past. We never did visit the house and its recreation, but we took comfort in knowing that it was making new memories and being recounted as a house from the past with a rich place in history.

We all knew that it would be the end of Cherry Street as we knew it when Aunt Marie was too old to care for herself and her home.

Once she was gone, Cherry Street would vanish into history, and after being forcibly moved to a nursing home for her own safety, Marie lost the will to live. So much of Marie was left behind; the familiar routines of life on Cherry Street, of an era about to vanish into the past, saddened all who knew what it meant to sit on the "back poach" and sip highballs and hear her coo, "Oh, daaahlin'." The chicken coop, horse barn, cow barn, the round house where the kitchen had once been, the greenhouse, the carport, and the white picket fence that circled the house all fell into disrepair. But inside everything was just as she had left it. In the kitchen stood the white linoleum table with the can opener affixed to the leg. The back porch where T-Fred, the yardman, ate his lunch was filled with canning jars, mops, and brooms. In the dining room, the silver was perched atop the sideboard, and in the corner a curio cabinet displayed etched glassware. In the hallway the record player with its top ajar was ready to play LPs, and there was a cabinet made of white beadboard and filled with medicines with faded labels and expiration dates from my father's childhood.

The squeaky floorboards and drafty rooms were no match for anyone who wanted to raise a family there, though we each fantasized about it. I was not a country girl, and Opelousas was no place for my siblings and me. We were raised and educated far from this world. Of the five Boudreaux boys, Ben was the only one who might have been able to take on the family home, but Opelousas was not the thriving town it once was and had a dwindling population. And it was under the jurisdiction of a notorious sheriff named Cat Doucet from 1936 to 1940 and again from 1952 to 1968, where it was a haven of gambling and prostitution. Opelousas was the site of one of the nation's two Yoo-hoo factories until it closed in 2009.

So when Ben married a girl from Rayne, the frog capital of the world, just forty miles from Opelousas, and moved to be near her family, our last hope for Cherry Street was gone. We all knew that once Marie was gone, so would go a prominent slice of our far-off world of Opelousas that all who had experienced never forgot. There were friends who met Marie maybe just once or had traveled to Opelousas to meet her and told the story of a crawfish boil, the way she captivated them with a charming expression or posed a sweetly naïve question that they remarked about forever. I heard those things over and over well into my adulthood. I tried to carry some of those with me; I even tied a floral polyester scarf around my neck that belonged to her and still call it Aunt Marie's scarf.

The house on Cherry Street where my fondest childhood memories are tucked into the crushed-velvet couches, worked into the oiled-leather saddles, or blowing in the warm southern breeze; sold the year after Aunt Marie's death in 1987. I have not been back to Opelousas since Each time I think there is a reason to go back to Opelousas, I remember that Aunt Marie isn't there, and then I realize how gone she really is. When Aunt

Marie died, Cherry Street went with her; the two could not exist separately. She gave life to an old home in a small town with no claim to fame or main attraction. She was the main attraction, even when, in her late eighties, her hearing and balance had gotten the best of her and she was content to sit in a chair off to the side and watch. I remember when my father told me it was time to sell the old homestead and the feeling of loss that we would never share another Easter around Aunt Marie's table after hunting for eggs in the vines of her tree. But after a few years of her being gone, I realized that Cherry Street existed in my mind, and to recreate it without her there would seem contrived. The "country" is my fondest childhood memory. It is a place emblazoned in my mind, and Aunt Marie is with me always.

Aunt Marie taught by example what it meant to be part of a southern family and to revel in the richness of our heritage. The rituals of Cherry Street live on in our hearts. The home we converged on once each year made us feel like we were never far from home, and even though the house stands empty now, the deserted rooms echo with our laughter, our hearts are part of the peeling wallpaper, and the furniture fills the rooms in our respective houses.

In the basement of my Colorado mountain home, there is a room full of furniture, a room in the country, the one belonging to Uncle Veazie, the quirky recluse. I can lie in Uncle Veazie's bed and imagine myself there again. I use the room as a guest bedroom and let guests tuck clothes away in the dresser with an attached mirror.

After Marie's death of natural causes at eighty-seven, my father eulogized his aunt, and at the end, my father choked back tears, something my brother, sister, and I had never seen, and just then we realized that there would never again be an Aunt Marie. Her coffin was adorned with bright-red roses, as chosen by my mother, who perhaps loved Aunt Marie more than we ever knew, for she loved my mother like the daughter she never had. Aunt Marie was the fabric of our colorful southern family, the matriarch who greeted all who came to her home, perched on the top step, holding the thickly painted screen door wide open and smiling. All those who experienced Aunt Marie and the "country," even if briefly, understood the magic of a time gone by. The vines of the oak tree reach out to us wherever we are, and Aunt Marie is wearing red in all of our dreams.

Twenty-Five

The Symposium

My Dad speaking at the 75th anniversary of the Huey Long Shooting

MY SISTER AND I arrived at the Baton Rouge airport for the symposium of the seventy-fifth anniversary of Huey Long's assassination, she from Boston where she taught middle school English, and I from Colorado where I commuted forty-five minutes to my teaching job at a local college. We were excited to see our southern family again, as there had been a long lapse since our yearly trip to Cherry Street. Aunt Marie was gone, and there were other reasons to visit; without Aunt Marie, there was a void that we did not want to acknowledge. It was as if the soul of the family was ripped out. We had all grown up; cousins had married, graduated from college, and moved on. We all wanted to remember it when Marie was there. To drive down Cherry Street and see the vacant lot where the home once stood, to see the overgrown pastures without any animals—it was too much for my siblings and me. The oak tree was still there, but its magic was gone. My father was seventy-five, so it had been that long since the assassination of Huey Long and the death of my grandfather.

My father still visited Opelousas to check in on his aunt Ida, whom he grew closer and closer to in their old ages. She was more like a sister to him, and they talked often of family matters. They owned non-producing oil wells, vacant gas stations, and dilapidated trailer parks together. A couple of Opelousas real estate barons. The allure of Opelousas was gone.

Yet here we were, there for the seventy-fifth anniversary of the death of Huey Long, where a panel of experts on the topic had converged to discuss whether time had changed anyone's minds on how the Kingfish died. My father, Carl Austin Weiss, was also in attendance. My mother stayed home, never one for any fanfare that had to do with my father and the killing of Huey Long. My brother was busy in his own medical practice in Upstate New York. My sister and I came to support the man who was just three months old when his father was gunned down by bodyguards, launching his name into infamy. His life's course was altered by this abrupt change of events, and his place as the son of a dedicated and beloved local doctor forced him to become a youngster without a father, living in France with his widowed mother as a way of escaping the blight on the family name.

On our travels from the airport, the signs of the Huey Long

era were everywhere. Near the baggage claim area, my sister and I gazed upon an airport display case of old photos that we had never seen before, and one was of our grandfather as he lay dead in a pool of his own blood. We laughed uncomfortably as we realized that we had been so shielded from this as youngsters coming back to the family home each year for the long-awaited Easter visit. We were carefully driven from the New Orleans airport in Aunt Marie's red Buick to the cattle guard while my father pointed out the sites from his adopted boyhood home. We passed the feed store, the Opelousas diner across from our great-uncle's law firm with the Pavy & Pavy sign, and the fields of planted soybeans on the family land. My father pointed (bending his index finger, as he had been told so many times by his uncle Bebe that it was impolite to point) to the same landmarks year after year in the small town of Opelousas that meant the world to this orphaned boy who was yanked from his home and reared in New York City, far from his country family. His aunts and uncles had their hearts broken, and they never quite healed, but none as much as his aunt Marie, who became a surrogate mother and protector of the little boy without a father.

But instead of never leaving the comfort of Cherry Street or the clutches of family on our yearly visits, on this September day we, as adults, now drove ourselves across unfamiliar territory. We crossed the Huey Long Bridge and the campus of LSU that Long doubled in size and greatness before his death. If we were not aware of it before, the magnitude of Huey Long's prominence in Louisiana could not be overlooked now by the two granddaughters of his alleged assassin.

In typical Cajun style, any event is a cause for celebration, and the Huey Long symposium was no different; after all, my family is Cajun, and parties are a way of life. We were greeted by family and friends for a weekend of reminiscing as we always did, yet this event was held at Aunt Ida's house where she and her family of five boys were reared, across town from Cherry Street. The only things missing were the back porch on Cherry Street where we all used to gather and our great-aunt Marie, who had been dead for eleven years now. After Marie died, we all feared that life in Opelousas would never be the same again, and while Marie's force of nature was missed and her porch full of chairs was now a field of weeds, we were back with our very southern roots. Our arrival was still met with a party, now at the boyhood home of our grown cousins.

The morning of the symposium was met with some anxious and nervous energy as relatives and friends from near and far made the drive to Baton Rouge to the governor's mansion. The room filled with people, including a large array of reporters and our young cousin Yvonne, named after her great-aunt, my grandmother, a young filmmaker who was devoting herself to documenting the event in a homegrown film of her own. She wanted the words of her grandmother, Ida, to tell the story of what life was like for the family who had been plunged into infamy. Our aunt Ida was the youngest of the family of six children born to Judge Henry Pavy. In 2010, the year of the seventy-fifth anniversary of the shooting of Huey Long and the death of her brother-in-law, eighty-four-year-old Ida had out-lived all of her siblings, as Marie was her senior by eleven years.

In front of the cameras was an auditorium-style seating where one side was filled with the Long family, ready to tell their stories, and on the other, the family of Carl Austin Weiss gathered to support the man who had been a boy when his father's name became synonymous with assassin. The panel of experts included several historians, a police chief, and friends and relatives of the two men who lost their lives seventy-five years ago. But when a man in a khaki suit, my father, stood at the podium in front of a photo projected on a large screen behind him of a spectacled man in his twenties bearing striking resemblance to him some fifty years earlier, the crowd shifted uneasily in their seats. My sister and I gazed intently at him, as we had never heard him tell the story of his father's demise. Rarely had we uttered a word about the series of events that led to our growing up as Yankees, as our Louisiana relatives referred to us. Yet here stood my father for nearly forty-five minutes, telling the crowd of Long and Pavy families what it was like to grow up knowing so little about the events of 1935, but having to bear the burden of them for so long.

When Yvonne left for France with her young son in 1938, her family was heartbroken and feared for her life, yet Yvonne felt she had to leave the turbulent South and the many threats to her life and her young son's. Yvonne had studied French at Sophie Newcomb in New Orleans and felt that France would be a cultural and personal awakening for her and a way to escape the reality of being the widow in a political assassination that was felt around the nation.

Many years later, my father received a box of letters written to his mother while living abroad, some from total strangers offering her kind words and sometimes money in the form of a ten-dollar bill, in the hopes that she was happy and healthy. Some told her that her husband was a hero for what he allegedly did. Here, seventy-five years later, a man who had never known his father stood in front of a largely sympathetic crowd, but also in front of the family of Huey P. Long, which included his grandson and several other Long family members, and talked about his father for the first time ever, while the audience was riveted by his words. My sister and I, along with our aunt Ida, who had been like a protective older sister to my father, took turns tearing up and clenching hands when he faltered ever so slightly.

Aunt Marie with her favorite nephew

TWENTY-SIX

The Other Side
of the Family

My brother with his son Carl Austin Weiss IV,
Uncle Tom Ed Weiss and my father

THE WEISS SIDE of the family was strangely quiet to us. Tom Ed
Weiss was just eighteen when word came over the radio waves
that his brother, ten years his senior, was guilty of a violent
crime. The tragic death of his brother left a scar a mile wide and
a mile deep that only showed signs of healing when his failing
health kept him from speaking out publicly at medical meetings and historical meetings about the innocence of his brother.
He is long gone now, but Tom Ed devoted much of his free

time from his own medical practice to keeping the history books from defaming his brother's name. The Weisses were a quiet family, very different from my grandmother's side. They were a long line of doctors who studied abroad and by all accounts were smart and serious. The photos are of men in horn-rimmed glasses with diplomas in medicines ranging from orthopedics to ear, nose, and throat specialties. We'd meet them on some of our Opelousas visits but did not want to leave the fun of the country to visit relatives. The Weiss family lost a son and a grandson when the shooting occurred.

While the Pavy family on Yvonne's side was able to put the ghosts at bay by never mentioning the event unless they had to, the Weiss family tried to remedy the situation in their lives by speaking about his innocence whenever they could. They had lost so much from the death of their son; they had even lost us, as my father did not know his father's side of the family as well as he should have. I think his uncle Tom Ed, his father's brother, was so tormented by the violent death and villainy of his brother that it pained him to see the boy, now a grown man who had never known his father. His older brother was his hero, and he tried to clear his name till the day he died. But the history books are slow to correct any wrongs that may have been written. The bodyguards were doing their jobs with overzealousness, protecting Huey Long from what they saw as a threat. Huey Long was ultimately killed by a bullet ricocheting off of the marble floor. It is hard to blame a marble floor for a murder.

It was only on the occasional visit to the South that we would plan a visit to Tom Ed and Catherine. We knew them by name only. The ghosts are everywhere for my family though;

with the death of those present when the event occurred, things change. No longer is the pain of the day my grandfather was named an alleged assassin present. Most of the principal players are dead, but on the recent visit to New Orleans with my family, I thought to myself that most of the people in Louisiana have studied their history and love their history. It is a state where culture and history are still prized by many, and this means that the shopkeepers, the hotel staff, and the historians all have some knowledge of the event that changed the lives of so many. When casually asked by the restaurateur serving me a bowl of crawfish étouffée just off Bourbon Street, "What brings you to New Orleans?" I take a deep breath and do not know which answer he wants, or what I want to tell him.

"Do you know who Huey Long is?" I ask.

He looks at me sideways as if to say, *Who doesn't?*

"My grandfather was the accused assassin," I say matter-of-factly. He prods me further and looks at me as if I do not understand what I have just said. I take my beans and rice and move on down the road. There is so much to see in New Orleans, and our ghost tour is about to begin on the streets of the French Quarter. This is not like our visit to the capitol in Baton Rouge the day before, when I asked the greeter to point us in the direction of the bullet holes that left divots in the marble.

I told her my grandfather was Carl Austin Weiss, and I don't think she heard me correctly because she announced in a high-pitched voice, "He didn't do it; he is the alleged assassin," hanging on the word *alleged* a bit longer than I needed.

TWENTY-SEVEN

When History Dies

MY FATHER DIED on the first day of August, surrounded by no one. He lay in a nursing home bed in sunny Florida where he had spent the last four years, living alone after the sudden death of my mother at age eighty. They say that dementia happens to those with higher IQs, and he had gone from a brilliant and gregarious man to a gaunt, almost mute person who had lost his ability to use the phone and had given up walking. He only spoke when spoken to, and while he could still speak French and dazzle strangers with his knowledge of history and stories of his past, he could no longer do the crossword puzzle and stopped reading the *New York Times* from cover to cover. In the end he lay in a hospital bed, looking at the bland walls of the nursing home. When remembering him, many said he was the most interesting man they had ever met—and not just because of the history of his life that involved his father dying in a highly publicized murder when he was three months old. The movies and books that were written about the murder of Huey Long and had become part of who my father was by default were not what made him interesting. It was not that he went to college at the age of fourteen or that he became a successful doctor. These things were certainly noteworthy, but it was the way he communicated and used words that made people stop and take notice. It was his curiosity and his full-scale knowledge of so many things. He could talk about so many different subjects. In a nutshell, he was incredibly well read and enlightened in so many subject matters. We would often say that he knew about things a mile wide and an inch deep. He could converse with anyone.

The event of his young life did have some impact on who my father was because he was raised by a single mother and had an unusual upbringing. There were so many adults in his life who spent so much time doting on him to make up for the lack of a father and for the villainy that his family lived with that he was never really treated like a child. He was treated like a miniature king. And so when he was grown and married and had children of his own, he did not know how to play or be anything but a king, but now he was larger and more fitting of this role. I remember very early on that I had to impress my father with big words, and that he really did not want to have anything to do with me until I could talk.

My brother eulogized him with these words: "Our father was an interesting man, as you all well know. He had a great intellect, and he was well educated. He spoke five languages and referenced Latin and Greek frequently to help make his point. He spoke of palindromes and epithets as well as syllogisms as second nature. He was well read, and he keenly enjoyed delving into complex topics, especially with an interest in history. He was an avid crossword puzzler with a vast array of knowledge from which to draw. We realized that he was not long for this world when his desire to finish the *New York Times* crossword puzzle was gone."

His death was a story for the *Boston Globe* and the *Acadiana*, and even the *New York Times* wrote a half page article on his passing. My sister, brother, and I were taken aback by the news outlets that called us for interviews to get a glimpse into the life of our father, but in the end the stories focused on what the death of his father meant to him and the life he led as the boy whose father was killed in a highly politicized alleged assassination. We answered the reporters' questions about who our father was as a man, but in the end, the stories for the newspapers were of the death of his father and the place in history it held. There was little mention of his accomplishments; it seemed that his only accomplishment was living out his life under the shroud of mystery and intrigue left after the death of Huey Long.

My brother eulogized my father in a warm and funny eulogy in the town we called home and where my father established Garden City Orthopedics and set broken bones and operated on generations of Long Islanders. My older brother was chosen as the family spokesperson because he, too, is named Carl Austin Weiss, with a III at the end. He and I were just thirteen months apart and shared the same high school friends and stories, yet his career path was laid out early, as his plan was always to be a doctor like his father. Perhaps it was expected. I remember his answer in his teens when asked what he wanted to be when he grew up. He would say, "Either a doctor or a janitor." For him, his career choice had been established as soon as he was born and named Carl Austin Weiss III. That became an important name after my grandfather was killed—the same name given to the little boy my mother birthed who died at just three days old, the name listed on several tombstones in the family plot adjacent to Aunt Marie's church where we paid a visit each Easter. My brother later told us how awkward it was to see his name on a miniature tombstone labeled for our dead brother, but perhaps that was when he realized the importance of his name. He eulogized his namesake on a hot day in August in a funeral home in the center of town where we grew up in Garden City, New York. His cremated remains were docked in the front of the room in a simple walnut box with his initials, CAW, seared into the top. My sister had scatter tubes to use later when we had the wherewithal to leave remnants of my father in the places he loved most, but for now, we needed to memorialize him among family and friends, to put an end to his four years of decline, and to remember him as he was before dementia had taken hold. In my brother's eulogy, he said, "One clear aspect of my dad's personality was bravado and boldness that can be best demonstrated in a story or two," and he rattled off the rules of being a measured surgeon. The rules as my brother learned them went like this:

"Rule number one: Never operate on family. Just not a good idea for many reasons," he read to the assembled family and friends, who listened eagerly, for my brother is a man of few words, unlike his father. He continued, "Rule number two: It is critically important to 'stay in bounds' and not wander off the beaten path." My brother's explanation for this rule would be revealed later in the eulogy. "This, too, helps avoid problems and complications. Built into this rule is that one must always operate in a facility that is capable of handling a particular situation and familiar to you." Another rule which makes perfect sense to even the non-medical person, he told the audience, "Rule number three: Cleanliness and antisepsis are paramount."

After mentioning these rules or tenets of good medical practice, Carl Austin Weiss III continued to tell the story of our father's loose relationship with "rules" as they applied to him and read, "It is with this understanding that my dad embarked on a mission to aid one of the cousins in Louisiana with an orthopedic issue. Cousin 'Dud,' as he was known to family and friends, was a three-hundred-pound, fifty-five-year-old lawyer by training who was an elected official at one point in the Louisiana legislature, living in a mobile home. He struggled with diabetes and HTN and venous stasis disease (leg ulcers) and was in need of a hip replacement. This is exactly what is considered a high-risk patient for any orthopedic procedure. Keeping in mind the three golden rules, Dad decided that the plan would be to fly to Louisiana in the V-tail Bonanza with the titanium hip implants in his briefcase. Also included in plastic bags were frozen squirrel carcasses intended to be prepared for a family barbecue while visiting. Opelousas General Hospital was chosen because it was a twenty-five-bed hospital with an ICU if one was needed. If ever there was surgery with danger written all over it, this was it," he continued. "So brazen was our father at times that we were cautious when he was around fire, or water, or weapons, or other things that could cause bodily harm or death."

We all knew that my father loved a challenge, that my father laughed at consequences, and that he was eminently a lucky man, as revealed in this story of rules broken by operating on an obese cousin with inadequate planning of a potentially deadly operation. My father became his cousin Dud's hero, and even he talked about the audacity he had in flying down in his little plane with dead squirrels in a bag. A fine squirrel roast ensued after a successful surgery, and Dad was hailed a hero, again for doing what really should not have been done. But then again, he could do no wrong to his loyal family. There was nothing that could tarnish my father in the eyes of his family. That was the life of the little boy whose life was shaped by sixty-one bullets and whose ashes will someday be scattered under the oak tree in Aunt Marie's yard, where time stood still, and family bonds were as impenetrable as the massive roots of a well-loved tree.

June 7, 1935-August 1st, 2019

Made in the USA
Columbia, SC
16 February 2022

55985810R00100